A VISUAL MOTOR GESTALT
TEST AND ITS CLINICAL USE

A VISUAL
MOTOR GESTALT TEST
AND ITS CLINICAL USE

LAURETTA BENDER, M.A., M.D.

SENIOR PSYCHIATRIST, PSYCHIATRIC DIVISION,
BELLEVUE HOSPITAL, NEW YORK
CLINICAL PROFESSOR OF PSYCHIATRY,
NEW YORK UNIVERSITY

RESEARCH MONOGRAPHS No. 3
AMERICAN ORTHOPSYCHIATRIC ASSOCIATION
LAWSON G. LOWREY, M.D., EDITOR

PUBLISHED BY
THE AMERICAN ORTHOPSYCHIATRIC ASSOCIATION
NEW YORK   ·   1938

Set up and printed by the
GEORGE BANTA COMPANY, INC.
MENASHA, WISCONSIN

Sixth Printing, 1953
Seventh Printing, 1955
Eighth Printing, 1957
Ninth Printing, 1958
Tenth Printing, 1960
Eleventh Printing, 1962
Twelfth Printing, 1965
Thirteenth Printing, 1966
Fourteenth Printing, 1967
Fifteenth Printing, 1969
Sixteenth Printing, 1971

FOREWORD

IN PRESENTING Dr. Bender's work as No. 3 of the Monograph Series, the Editor has borne in mind the essential purposes of the Association in establishing the Series. These include the publication of contributions which present unusual techniques or findings of particular interest to those in the field of the study and treatment of behavior and personality problems. Such studies would be based upon original work too detailed for publication in The Journal.

This volume on "A Visual Motor Gestalt Test and its Clinical Use" represents a unique and important contribution to the field. It is, therefore, with considerable pride and pleasure that we present this volume.

LAWSON G. LOWREY
Editor

PREFACE

GESTALT PSYCHOLOGY as it has been developed by the work of Wertheimer, Köhler and Koffka has given a new impetus to psychology. It has given us a new insight into the relation between the whole and its parts and has shown that perception cannot be understood as the summation of single sensations. It has stated that sensory fields are replete with qualities and properties which cannot be understood if one takes sensations as the units. The organism does not react to local stimuli by local events but reacts to constellations of stimuli by a total process which is the response of the whole organism to the total situation. Such a process regulates itself and distributes itself dynamically. Gestalt psychology has stressed the dynamic inner factor, the self regulation in perception. Previous experience cannot explain the existence of segregated units in experience as the grouping of points and lines, for instance, in the configurations of stars. It furthermore cannot determine what will be in the foreground and what will be in the background of one's perceptual experience. This is determined by the total situation. Simple connotations like figure, hole, foreground, background, group, open, closed, circle, complete and incomplete, starting, beginning, end, good gestalt or bad gestalt gain a new significance. Children would not learn how to organize a visual field even after years of trial and error.

Gestalt psychology has put its emphasis on the perceptive process; however, it has had the conviction that its basic principals are also valid in other realms of psychic life. Studies have been made on configuration, will and action.

American psychology and psychiatry has tended to reject the mechanical psychological theories and has stressed the dynamic factors of the total situation. It has, furthermore, developed the concept of pattern which is the result of the interplay of the dynamic organization of the total organism with the situation.

Gestalt psychology means indeed an important step forward stressing the total reaction and the total situation. It has abolished the mechanical theory of perception and association. Although it stresses the dynamic in contrast to the static experiences it has not always seen that these dynamics are built on previous experiences, human strivings and on trial and error. It has over-rated the inner factors of development and over-rated the rigidity of configurations. Organization gets its final meaning only in relation to concrete situations of life which adapt the patterns to the actions and experimentations of individuals. In the field of per-

vii

ception gestalt psychology has deepened our insight considerably and is a new definite proof for the validity of a dynamic psychology and complements the fundamental ideas of American Psychiatry.

The deep conviction of the intrinsic value of the basic ideas of gestalt psychology has led Dr. Bender to investigate a problem which promises to relate the field of perception to the problem of the personality and its dynamic patterns.

Dr. Bender's book appreciates fully the work done by gestalt psychologists. The method which she has developed, namely, copying of gestalt forms, broadens immediately the field of observation. Her method does not merely answer the question what the individual perceives but answers also the question what does the individual use his perception for? Her method allows, therefore, a much more direct expression of the biological factors than experiments in which the subjects merely describe their experiences. Psychological experimentation often artificially disrupts perception and motility. This is avoided here by the simple expedient that the individual draws what he perceives.

I see in this one of the main reasons for the wealth of interesting results which this book contains. It approaches the fundamental problems of perception and action from a new angle. It shows the primitive forms of experience and the maturation process in the course of development. It shows the continuous interplay between motor and sensory factors. A new world of primitive perception opens up. It has even been possible to standardize the development of the visual motor gestalt function. Her investigations show furthermore the close relation of the development of optic form to visual imagination. It is of particular interest that the primitive forms of visual motor experience make their appearance also when the time of perception is shortened. One comes to the impression that every individual in almost every experience passes through the whole maturation process through which the individual developed during his childhood. I consider these results as fundamental for the problem of perception.

However, this is a test which offers more than theoretical interest. It gives a correct estimate of visual motor development which in general goes parallel to the mental development of the child. It allows an insight into the different forms of developmental disturbance and points to a differentiation between various forms of mental deficiency.

Gestalt psychology has often been used in psychopathology and valuable results have increased our insight into the psychopathology of perception. However, to the best of my knowledge, this is the first systematic approach to this problem. The results obtained in schizophrenia, manic depressive psychosis, aphasias and organic brain diseases get their full meaning when one compares them with the standardized lines of development. Personal experience has taught me that the clinical value of the test is very great. It may allow a differential diagnosis between organic deterioration, so-called functional mental disease and malingering.

Dr. Bender does not forget that gestalt patterns are experiences of an individual who has problems and that the final configuration of experience is not merely a problem of perception but a problem of personality. This becomes particularly clear when one studies the gestalt function in neurotics.

I have been impressed by this work from its very beginning. I think it opens up important vistas. It will help the psychologist and the psychiatrist; it will interest everybody who is interested in fundamental problems of development. I must confess I have some family pride in this work.

PAUL SCHILDER, M.D., PH.D.,
Research Professor of Psychiatry,
New York University,
Clinical Director, Psychiatric
Division, Bellevue Hospital,
New York City

New York, New York
September, 1938

CONTENTS

PART I. THEORETICAL DATA

CHAPTER I

INTRODUCTION

THE CLASSICAL teachings of the gestalt school are represented in the works of Wertheimer, Koffka and Köhler, formerly referred to as the Berlin school. At the present time, however, all these men are in the United States. Their teachings are built upon relatively static concepts. That their attempts to erect a psychological system have not met with success are due largely to failures in the fields of personality psychology and abnormal psychology. The best results have been obtained in the field of perceptual psychology, although Lewin has emphasized the importance of the need for closing a gestalt or completing an experience. The more dynamic teachings of Sander have emphasized the part which the individual contributes to the finally experienced gestalten. Schilder has gone further and has shown that the motor factor cannot be ignored. Schilder also introduces the gestalt concept in his study of the body image and recognizes the body image as an experienced gestalt which is everchanging and never static; it is constantly disrupted and reconstructed from new life situations. Further than this gestalt psychology has not taken us for it has failed to account for the drives and tendencies of human conducts, growths and regressions.

In this book no effort will be made to review the classical teachings of gestalt psychology; Koffka and Hartmann and many others whose publications are available in English as well as German, have recently dealt with this subject in sufficient detail.

In this book clinical material is offered. Visually perceived configurations first used by Wertheimer in his experimentations with visual gestalten have been offered to children and adults and mentally defective and mentally sick patients with the request that they be copied. The final product is a visual motor pattern which reveals modifications in the original pattern by the integrating mechanism of the individual who has experienced it.

The gestalt function may be defined as that function of the integrated organism whereby it responds to a given constellation of stimuli as a whole; the response itself being a constellation, or pattern, or gestalt. All integrative processes within the nervous system occur in constellations, or patterns, or gestalten. Integration occurs not by summation or subtraction or association but by differentiation, or by increasing or decreasing the internal complexity of the pattern in its setting. It appears that an integrated organism never responds in any other way. The whole setting of the stimulus and the whole integrative state of the organism determine the pattern of the response. Starting with this thesis, one may use the given stimulating constellation in more or less similar settings and study the gestalt function in various pathological integrative conditions in different organic and functional nervous and mental disorders. Such has been the technique that was employed in this study. Any pattern in any sensory field may be regarded as a potential stimulus. Visual motor patterns have proved most satisfactory, because the visual field most readily adapts itself to experimental study and especially because the sick patient can usually cooperate with the simple test of copying a few test forms.

Nine of Wertheimer's original patterns were chosen from his classical 1923 paper (*See Plate 1*).

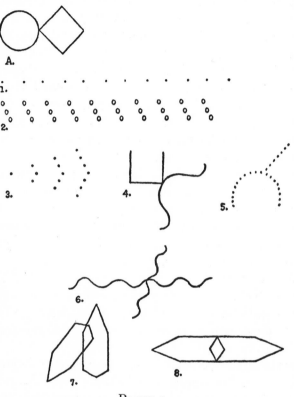

PLATE I

Figure A was chosen as an introductory figure because it soon became evident that it was readily experienced as closed figures on a background. According to Wertheimer, this configuration is recognized as two contingent figures because each represents a "gute gestalt". This principle overrules the principle that parts which are closer together are usually seen together. In this instance, the contiguous parts of the circle and square are closer to each other than the two sides of the square. Figure 1, according to Wertheimer, should be so perceived that the dots appear as a series of pairs determined by the shortest distance, or with "remnants" left over at each end. Such a pairing would be more readily perceived if the differences in the distances had been greater. This is an example of a gestalt formed on the principle of the proximity of parts. Figure 2, according to Wertheimer, is perceived usually as a series of short slanting lines consisting of three units so arranged that the lines slant from left above to right below. It is also determined on the principle of proximity of parts. This is also true of Fig. 3. Figure 4 is ordinarily perceived as two units determined by the principle of continuity of geometrical or internal organization; the open square with the bell-shaped form at the lower right-hand corner. The same principle holds for the introductory Fig. A and also for Fig. 5 which is seen as an incomplete circle with an upright slanting stroke made in dotted lines. Figure 6 is seen as two sinusoidal lines with different wave lengths, crossing each other at a slant. Figures 7 and 8 are two configurations made up of the same units, but they are rarely perceived as such, because in Fig. 8 the principle of continuity of geometric forms prevails—which in this instance is a straight line at the top and bottom of the figure.

Gestalt psychology claims that organized units or structuralized configurations are the primary forms of biological reactions at least at the psychological level of animal behavior, and that in the sensory field these organized units or gestalten correspond to configurations of the stimulating world.

There is an innate tendency to experience gestalten (Schilder) not only as wholes which are greater than their parts (Wertheimer, Koffka, Köhler) but in the state of becoming (Eddington) which integrates the configuration not only in space but in time. Furthermore, in the act of perceiving the gestalt the individual contributes to the configuration. The final gestalt is, therefore, composed of the original pattern in space (visual pattern), the temporal factor of becoming and the personal-sensory-motor factor. The resulting gestalt is also more than the sum of all these factors. There is a tendency not only to perceive gestalten but to complete gestalten and to reorganize them in accordance with principles biologically determined by the sensory motor pattern of action. This pattern of action may be expected to vary in different maturation or growth levels and in pathological states organically or functionally determined.

There is a tendency for continuous experimentation with the external stimulating pattern and the action tendencies of the sensory-motor-conceptional person. The final pattern may represent a momentary point of equilibrium between the balancing function and is liable to change.

The factor of becoming is present in the physical world (Eddington).

It accounts for the continuous integrating physical processes and tendencies. It is also present in the individual personality. There it also accounts for tendencies to action and drives. In the final analysis the two are the same working towards the necessity for completing gestalten in all the realms of nature.

Working with and against the tendency of becoming, are the destructive forces whereby all gestalten are simplified or destroyed. This tendency is seen in the experimental work brought forth in this book when the individual reacting to the stimulus is a deviate. Even in these individuals, the drive to experience complete gestalten and to contribute to the integration of gestalten are always present. A gestalt is always experienced, but a more primitive form tends to emerge still whole in itself and still greater than the sum of all its parts.

By this experimentation, a mass of data has been accumulated which is offered as a contribution to the psychology of gestalt, to the psychology of the functioning of the personality, and to the science of clinical medicine. Furthermore, it will be the effort of the author to indicate in what way this new data adds new understanding to the functions of the normal mind and to various forms of pathological mental states.

The author has freely used parts of papers already published in the Archives of Neurology and Psychiatry, The Journal of Psychoasthenics, and The Pedagogical Seminary and Journal of Genetic Psychology, for which appreciation is expressed.

CHAPTER II

MATURATION PROCESSES IN CHILDREN
AND THE MOTOR FACTOR*

IT IS IMPORTANT to see how gestalten arise genetically in children and what the processes of maturation are. It is quite evident that the infant does not experience perception as the adult does. Nevertheless, the school child who is able to read and write must have visual motor experiences similar to the adult. Dorothy (*Plate 2*) who was a bright fourteen year old girl, copied the test forms as a normal superior adult would be expected to do. We shall now be interested in observing the manner in which the small child must pass through many stages of maturation before it is able to achieve this stage of efficiency.

We already know that the first drawings of children (See Goodenough for bibliography) are scribblings that represent pure motor play. These are done for the pleasure of the motor expression, the scribbled pictures being a by-product and having no meaning. They are performed by large arm movements in a dextrad, clockwise whirl or pendulum waves if the child uses its right hand, and in sinistrad, counter-clockwise whirls if the left hand is used. Soon the child will produce such scribblings on command for any suggested picture or in response to any test form offered, and then call them by some other name if it so pleases him. Such are the scribblings of Eva at two years and eight months, when asked to draw a man and to copy the test forms (*Plate 2*). She was delighted with the fun of the game and called the resulting scribbles, "ropes". At two years and eleven months, Sara already showed a tendency to inhibit her scribblings to a more continuous form of loop. Furthermore, she could be influenced by watching the examiner perform the motor act of drawing some new figures rather than by the figures which were offered her to copy. She made arm movements similar to the examiner's, about the sample form of Fig. A which represents a well inhibited part of a loop accomplished in one arm stroke. She perseverated this response several times with great joy and tended to emphasize the single stroke aspect of the game. She offered the same response for the next figure (Fig. 1), although it was

* Taken in part from "Gestalt Function in Mental Defect" read before the 57th Annual Session of the American Association on Mental Deficiency in Boston, Mass., May 29–June 3, 1933, and published in the Proceedings of this Association, or the Journal of Psychoasthenics.

PLATE 2

entirely inappropriate. Then she was shown how to make dots. The motor part of the dot-making game pleased her very much. She emphasized the stab of the pencil into the paper. Then she made a loop form out of dots instead of by means of the single arm movement. At this stage she gained a sudden insight into the game as a whole. She discovered that some of the figures were made of single stroke loops and some were made of dotted loops. For the next several figures she responded accordingly without further help. There is certainly some resemblance in Figs. 4, 5 and 6, especially in Fig. 6 where the long horizontal loop doubled back and crossed itself in the middle. However, the examiner could not resist trying to show her how to make Fig. 6. Sara observed the zigzag arm movement. She tried it herself and was pleased with the result. She had also observed that there were two parts to the movement, that one started and stopped again, but she could not properly orient the two zigzag lines so that they would cross. In Figs. 7 and 8 we see how well Sara really understood the problem and how well she used the modified form of her loop to express the gestalt principles implied in the test forms, except that in Fig. 7 she showed a concentric relationship of the two loops which is the most primitive form of a relationship of any two parts in a whole. Of course, the very simplest visual motor gestalt relationship is an enclosed loop on a background. As we have seen, the principle of this relationship arises from the motor behavior of the small child which adapts itself to resemble the stimulus perceived in the optic field.

Eleanor, who was three years and six months old, understood the use of loops very well. However, she sometimes spoiled her results by an uninhibited tendency to closures. She could make dots in Fig. 1 only after she was shown how, but she gave them up and continued to experiment with loops and parts of loops. In Fig. A she made two loops and showed their relationship by a graphic connection. This tendency to graphically depict relationships occurs very often. She was not satisfied with her results and tried to increase the inhibition of both loops, but that did not work either. The third effort in which she showed a real differentiation in the two parts of the figure is very good. She looped the loop freely in the first part and in the second part constructed a figure with several little parts of loops, the exact number of which did not bother her. Dots were made in Fig. 1 in imitation of the examiner. She experimented some with little loops in Fig. 2, but was not entirely satisfied and finally called one of them "a man" and then stopped. Figure 3 is a single enclosed loop resembling the whole figure on a background. Figure 4 shows the adjacent relationship of the two parts, one loop less round than the other but both enclosed. Figure 5 shows this overwhelming tendency to closures, which was best observed by watching the child perform the test. The round loop was made and the upper right-hand dash was added so that the figure would have been excellent even though her arc was a complete circle, if only she had stopped there. She studied it several seconds in doubt and finally completed the right-hand side of the figure. The close resemblance to Fig. A and parts of Fig. 2 will be noted. This is the infantile tendency to utilize a similarly constructed form for different purposes. In Fig. 6, the lower wavy line was drawn and an effort was made to cross it with one little line, but after some hesitation she enclosed the whole figure. A second effort was better, due to the inhibition of primitive tendencies, but the crossing was still difficult and as a result occurs at the tip end of the line. Figure 7 resembles A, 2 and 5, but was modified to adapt better to the form offered. Figure 8 is the typical response of the young child, easily done because it represents the concentric relationship of two enclosed figures.

Eva at the age of three years and eight months, just one year after she made her scribbled "ropes" showed how much she had matured in her ability to control her scribblings. She represents Fig. A as two adjacent loops; Fig. 1 as a series of loops until she is shown how to make dots; Fig. 2 as a series of little loops; Fig. 3 as a mass of dots; Fig. 4 as two loop segments (somewhat disoriented in their relationship to each other); Fig. 5 as a mass of dots; Fig. 6 as one loop crossing another; Fig. 7 as two related loops, and Fig. 8 as possibly a perseveration of the line she drew in Fig. 7.

Evelyn at the age of three years and nine months shows considerable motor contol and a tendency to differentiate the different forms and gestalt principles. First, we see the kind of man she can draw. This man scores her a mental age of four years on the Goodenough scale. Figure A is a modification of this man. Figure 2 is of special interest as it shows that the child does not experience this figure in accordance with the Wertheimer laws, but as a horizontal series of loops. Eva was satisfied with one series, but Evelyn had discovered that there are three horizontal series, though their exact relationship to each other is not so important. Figure 3 is always the most difficult figure. She sees it only as a series of dots. Figure 4 is somewhat disoriented; Fig. 5 is a little sketchy but the principle is all there; Fig. 6 was difficult to cross but it was accomplished; in Figs. 7 and 8, the proper relationships, which is the first essential in gestalten, are shown, although the exact sizes, distances, and details of shape are not represented.

In the study of these visual motor patterns in children from two and one-half to four years, we may deduct the following principles: scribbling is at first a motor activity. It may acquire significance after production. It tends to take on a differentiated form by inhibition into single closed loops or parts of loops. Patterns or gestalten are formed by combinations of those which are adapted to resemble the perceived stimulus or to represent it symbolically. The child finds it difficult to reproduce patterns, but by various motor experimentations pictures are produced which may finally represent the pattern desired. It is easier for the child to imitate the movements of another person so that scribbling may be limited to single arm movements, to dashes, dots, and zigzags. Once these are learned by motor imitation or experimentation, they may be more freely used to resemble test figures. Thus, any dotted form may call forth the motor behavior that produces dots, but the tendency may still persist to produce them in loop formation or masses or series. An enclosed loop is the basis of all perceived form. There is also a tendency to perseverate any one learned (even if self-discovered) pattern wherever adaptable to other perceived figures, or, at the most primitive level to use the first experienced form or behavior pattern in response to any figure that is offered. This merely represents to the child a stimulus that calls forth the pattern. Direction, especially dextrad horizontal direction in the right-handed child, is more important than distance or size. It is more overwhelming than Wertheimer's principles of proximity (as in Fig. 2), or similarity of parts. This predominance of the directional factor is probably due in part to motor features, and in part to the principle that the optic field is organized on movement. Such concepts as "series" and "masses" are more readily grasped by children than absolute number or size. Wertheimer's principle of continuity is important to the extent that it involves direction and series; his principle of "gute gestalt" and natural geometrical figures are important to the extent that they arise out of the primitive loop. Otherwise the principles of gestalt given by Wertheimer do not apply to the genesis of gestalt in the maturation of the child's visual motor patterns.

There is a rapid differentiation of form between the ages of four and seven years (*Plate 3*). This is the age that children are sent to school and expected to learn to read and write. Henrietta who was four years and eight months old, reproduced the test figures in such a way that they closely resemble them. Figure A is two closed forms, the right-sided one less round but the distance between the two is not a matter of importance to her. Figure 1 is a series of little dash-like dots. Figure 2 is three hori-

Normal Children 4 yrs to 6 yrs

PLATE 3

zontal series of little loops. Figure 3 is only a series of dots to her; Fig. 4 consists of two open forms widely separated as in Fig. A. Figure 5 is quite well done. Figure 6 expresses the crossed relationship in its simplest form. Figures 7 and 8 show the side to side and concentric relationship of primitive loops. It will be noted that any slanting or oblique relationships are not depicted at this maturation level. Norman at the age of four years and eleven months used some form of the loop or enclosed figure in all his responses. In Fig. A he has produced a pretty good square although not obliquely oriented. Figure 1 is a series of tiny loops, but there is no pairing. In Fig. 2 for the first time we see the vertical series of three loops but there is no slanting. Figure 3 is still too difficult for him. Figure 4 is a modification of Fig. A. Figure 5 shows an interesting displacement of the dash; perhaps the very effort it required for this child to make a dash when he was still dealing in loops displaced it. In Fig. 6 he got the idea of two wavy lines but he could not cross them. In comparing this with the previous child, we see that often a child can get one new principle in a gestalt but he cannot combine two of them in the same gestalt.

Leon at five years shows several advances in progress. In an effort to slant the vertical series in Fig. 2 he has displaced the whole figure. Figure 3 shows the first real effort to produce this pattern. It is a series of concentric dotted curves, the number of series or the number of dots in each series appearing not to matter. Figure 6 is a crossed wavy line but the crossing is not slanted. There is, however, an oblique over-lap in Fig. 7.

Paul at six years and five months made a real diamond in Fig. A and showed a better accomplishment in details of relationships in Figs. 3, 4, 5, 7 and 8 than any of the younger children but still he always uses loops instead of dots, although he sometimes fills in the loops to make them look like dots. He was unable to cross the lines in Fig. 6 or angulate those in Fig. 3. Richard at the age of seven years and ten months does all these things, except that even yet his dots resemble little loops and some of his slanting relationships are not very accurate and the pairing does not occur in Fig. 1. Perfection in size, shape, distances and motor control is still not so good as it was in the work of the fourteen year old Dorothy first shown.

It will appear from these experiments that visual motor patterns arise from motor behavior that is modified by the characteristics of the visual field. This is organized about the primitive enclosed loop with directional tendencies (usually dextrad and horizontal at first) and perseverative behavior. There is a constant interplay or integration between the motor and sensory features which can never be separated, though one or the other may advance more rapidly than the other in the maturation process and appear for a time to dominate any given stage in the evolution of the gestalt.

Koffka has pointed out that even during development, all motor acquisitions have a sensory component. It is also held that movement is a necessary condition for perception, at least in the primitive stages of development (Katz). Thus the organism is indeed an organism-as-a-whole or no organism at all. Köhler brings forth the point that behavior is not the response of the organism to the stimulus, but it is the response of the organism to its own sensory organization of the stimulus. The child, therefore, responds to a much more simply conceived world than does the adult. Hartmann speaks of the greater dynamic unity of the child making the isolation of a single action more difficult than for the adult. He quotes Köhler's color-box experiment with his three year old daughter to show that the native and primitive perceptual responses in children stress totals and wholes. Similar principles may be demonstrated in spontaneous drawings of children.

In 1931,* I became interested in the spontaneous production of children in the chalk drawings on sidewalks and the open pavements of parks. The numerous small parks that dot the East Side of New York afford a great wealth of material, as during the pleasant weather of the spring and fall they are always covered with the drawings of the neighborhood children. Apparently no systematic studies of such drawings have ever been made. They present several advantages over the usual paper-and-pencil or slate drawings. One advantage is their absolute spontaneity. The children draw for the fun of the thing and with apparently no other goal in view than the immediate joy of activity and production, except in the cases of sidewalk games such as hopscotch, when the drawings afford the setting for the games.

The sidewalk drawings also give an opportunity to study drawings produced under different motor conditions. The child is usually either sitting or kneeling on the ground on which he is drawing, or leaning over from a standing position, or even precariously balancing himself on roller skates and drawing with large arm sweeps. But the pictures produced in these ways are quite similar to those described so extensively in the literature from the usual paper-and-pencil method.

Perhaps the most important differences are dependent upon the un-

* Taken in part from "Gestalt Principles in Sidewalk Drawings and Games of Children" from The Pedagogical Seminary and Journal of Genetic Psychology, 1932, 41, 192–210.

limited amount of space. A child with plenty of chalk, with pavement all about him, with plenty of time, and totally unconscious of any supervision, rarely draws a complete isolated figure. He draws and draws and scribbles all over the place, delighted when his scribbles display some unexpected form; experimenting with this, he modifies it first this way and then that by some such simple variation as enlarging a loop or extending a line, often leaving some fragment of a design incomplete in order to try a new variation. He may for some reason leave this place and at some subsequent time take up the game again in some new area, or other playmates may adopt his idea and play with it in their own way. Thus definite schools of design may prevail in a neighborhood for days at a time. Of great interest are these drawings that are scattered lavishly on the sidewalk in

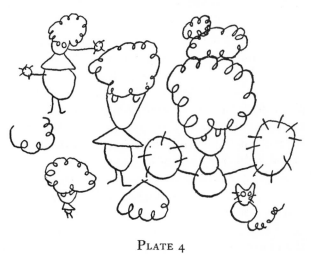

PLATE 4

a spirit of experimentation. In *Plate 4* we see a study in whirligigs, sometimes just for their own sake, as on the left border, or as the tail of a cat, as in the lower right-hand corner, but more often as the central theme in a human figure in which they are featured as the hair. The rest of the body is suppressed in different ways; once, the legs and feet are missing but the hands are exaggerated, again the arms are missing but the legs are better represented, but at best are unimportant as compared to the hair. The body is always shown in a similar way, as is also the face, in which only the eyes appear as features. Also in the cat a similar pattern is shown. In different parts of the same park different modifications of this design were seen and continued to appear for several days. One might look upon this as a period in which the school of whirligigs dominated the art tendencies in this particular locality.

It certainly becomes evident that the satisfaction derived from these drawings is largely a motor one. This is especially true of the smaller children but it also occurs in the older ones. They may simply make large arm movements with swaying circular lines until they have filled all the nearby space or used up all of the available chalk. Usually, any given area is filled with the results of many different activities as well as the better organized pictures of older children. Loops and circles in many variations are gradually worked into more elaborate designs. Sully has emphasized that the first designs are circular and lunar forms of the human face. Shinn recognized O's first at twelve months and C's and Q's soon after. Dora Musold working under Vokelt, tested children for their ability to discriminate between spheres, surface circles, contour circles and straight lines. She found that the small children had a better discrimination for spheres than adults or older children, but a much poorer discrimination for straight lines. The child is first acquainted with his own and his mother's body, his own feces, his mother's breast and his mother's face. Sully has made the interesting comment that the earliest pictorial forms have embryonic characteristics. We are impressed with the possibility that the postural model of the body (Schilder) is the first perceptual experience and helps to determine the organization of the visual field, for as Koffka says, "it is not the simplest forms but those biologically most important which are first evident in infantile perception". However, the visual field may have underlying physiological features of its own that determine its organization into movements, into whirling, circular, and wavy type. Kanner and Schilder have shown that the characteristic properties of optic imagery are movements of a wavy and circular type with scintillations and multiplications or fading and diffusing of the image, or part of it, and participation of the background in the same process. The tedious problem of explaining how form first begins (Koffka, 1935) would be solved if it were better recognized that movement and perception cannot be separated, and in studying the genesis of form in the perception of children we find that it is the outgrowth of motion.

In this same connection I want also to discuss a group of children's sidewalk games known as hopscotch. Hopscotch is a game that has several variations, but after watching the children play it, it becomes evident that the variations are dependent upon the different age levels; that is, on the maturation levels of the perceptual motor patterns. Of course, this is not absolute, as older children will sometimes play with a younger group, and vice versa; and older children will sometimes revert to simpler forms, and younger children will sometimes emulate their elders. But, in general, small tots just able to hop on one leg, will make a simple whirl design on the pavements, mark it off in blocks (*Plate 5*, Fig. 1) and hop from block to block until they reach the center. The aim is always to hop on one foot, without putting the other foot down and without touching a line. Sometimes a small stone or other object is kicked from one space to the next, but this is not an essential part of the game. The size of the loop depends upon the abilities of the members of the group and it is readily enlarged by adding to the open end. This is a very simple game but apparently affords a good deal of satisfaction for tots of four to six or seven years of age. One sees in this an almost pure example of a perceptional motor game involving the principles of a visual pattern of the primitive whirl type and a motor pattern involving the simplest rhythmic hopping in a whirling direction. Whirling is an activity which young children apparently enjoy very much and which is probably dependent upon their primitive postural reflexes and vestibular sensations (Schilder, *Brain and Personality*), motor impulses, and perceptual principles. Similar whirling games were also played by Köhler's apes.

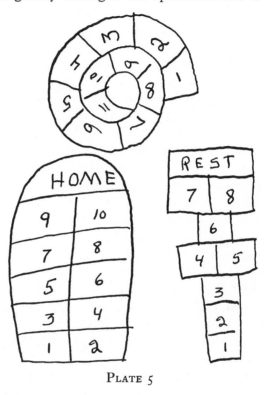

PLATE 5

The more mature children made a hopscotch design like Fig. 2 in *Plate 5*. The general outline is more rectangular, although it is rounded at the top where "Heaven" or "Home" or "Rest" is located. It is marked off by cross lines into eight or ten square sections. The aim here is more complex. A block is always used and the child hops and kicks the block from one square to the next until it reaches the top without touching a line or putting down the other foot; the block must be kicked each time into the proper square without stopping on a line. This involves several more complicated processes. The primitive circular form has organization only from the periphery to the center and in a clock-wise or counter-clock-wise direction. But in this second form we have a top and bottom, and left and right side, and there are also straight lines crossing each other. The motor pattern requires a better adaptation and includes the accurate control of an inanimate object and also back-and-forth direction.

A still more sophisticated form of this game is played by girls of eight to ten years of age. They make a design such as is seen in Fig. 3 of *Plate 5*. Here the pattern includes the alternate position of form, and the motor activity includes an extra step over the paired spaces where the girls will put both feet down over the paired spaces between each hop in the individual spaces, kicking the block from one space to the next.

The child's early activities in spontaneous drawings, games and various forms of play represent experiments in form, spatial relationships, rhythms and temporal relationships and various physical forces such as gravity. This has already been discussed in a paper by Schilder and myself, "Form as a Principle in the Play of Children." This is in keeping with Isaacs' teachings that the child has a disinterested drive for knowledge as such and is in contrast to the teachings of Piaget who sees in all the early behavior of the child egocentric tendencies, and the teachings of Melanie Klein for whom the child's love of knowledge or epistophilic drives is a drive for sex knowledge, and for both of which the child's early drives are essentially instinctual in the sense of emotional. In the children's drawings, play, and activities, they show their drive to experience or experiment with physical phenomena, while in their *why* question they show their drive for cognitive experiments of the same nature. Susan Isaacs has emphasized this early drive for knowledge, but is inclined to look upon it as a drive for the absolute due to fear, insecurity and incomplete or erroneous knowledge. My experiments, on the other hand, would lead to the conclusion that the child actually experiments with the different phenomena, getting satisfaction with each new experience which is complete enough for that stage of maturation of the developing organism growing from preceding experience level. There is, moreover, a continuous reaching out for new experiments in which the child freely gives himself so that his activities become an active part of the knowledge obtained. This becomes a continually expanding "gestaltung" which is continually reshaping itself in the experience of the growing child, and is both experienced by and produced by the child. It may be particularly well seen in the drawing of these gestalt forms at different age levels that the child accepts them not as absolute truths or patterns of the forms which are displayed, but that they represent constellations of stimuli to which different organisms react and experience in different ways, and that the reaction or experience of each child is complete and satisfactory for him.

CHAPTER III

LOW GRADE DEFECTIVES AND THE BIOLOGICAL BACKGROUND FOR FORM AND SPACE

IF NOW WE STUDY the responses of defective adults in which the motor reaction pattern appears mature but in which the intellectual level is very low, we may get responses which come nearer to primitive perceptual patterns. Retardation in maturation seems to simplify the pattern reaction somewhat as the tachistoscope exposure, it seems to eliminate the integration of the temporal factor which modifies the perceptual experience. Working with the low grade adult defectives was a part of my earliest experimenting with the visual motor gestalt function.

RESULTS

Mentally Defective Persons. A subject with a mental age between 1 and 2 years responded to her own name, walked and kept herself clean, but could not talk. She made forms on the paper of her own liking (*Plate 6*) which are of considerable interest, especially in the light of productions of the progressively higher mental levels. Her production is shown in *Plate 6*. It does not resemble the copy, but is seen to resemble closely handwriting in some unknown language. It had no evident meaning for this patient, but still it is made up of all the elements of written language and is

PLATE 6

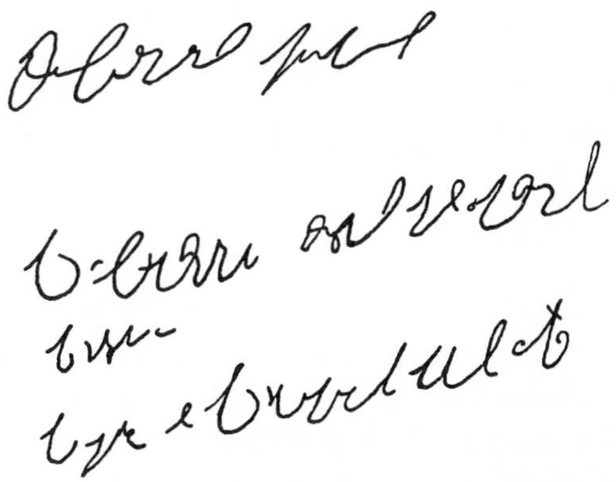

broken into units closely resembling words. One might think that she had previously seen and learned to imitate handwriting, but when one observes that these simple minds cannot copy forms considerably simpler than this, and that they are not capable of any such memory feat, it is realized that this is not possible. It is of interest, however, that Ament, in studying the spontaneous and copied productions of small children, showed that children between the ages of 2 and 4 produce meaningless scribblings of a similar sort. The examples given by him are considerably cruder than the productions in *Plate 6*, owing, no doubt, to the better developed motor control of the adult who is mentally defective. Ament claimed that the child's scribblings are probably an imitation or copy of some adult writing, but inconsistently enough went on to show that in the next higher mental levels the children are unable to copy or imitate, but make forms without thought or resemblance to the copy in front of them and are unable to recognize or name their own productions. It may be, therefore, that at this low level the productions are the product of a motility response as, indeed, is claimed by Prinzhorn who stated that in young children drawings are merely the expression of joy in rhythmic movement, and that the productions have no meaning for them. Also Gaupp said that in children from 1 to 3 years old scratches and scribblings are only an expression of activity, and that meaning of form or ability to copy does not appear until 3 to 4 years of age.

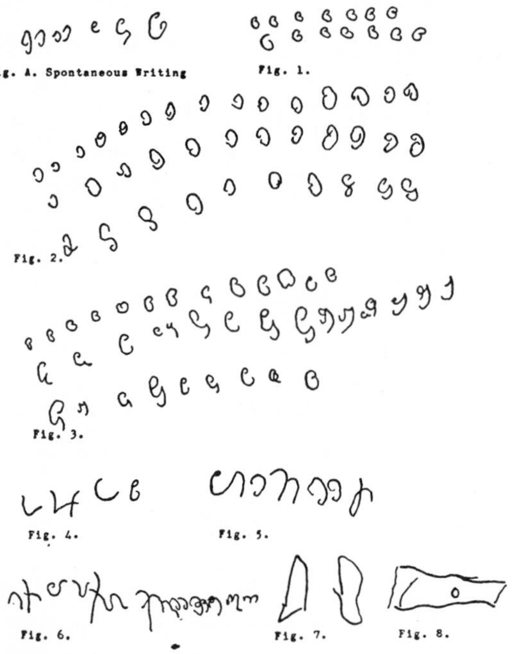

Fig. A. Spontaneous Writing   Fig. 1.

Fig. 2.

Fig. 3.

Fig. 4.   Fig. 5.

Fig. 6.   Fig. 7.   Fig. 8.

PLATE 7

A woman with a mental age of about 3 years was able to understand instructions and to endeavor to copy the forms that were presented to her. Her results are shown in *Plate 7*. First is seen some of her spontaneous writing, which closely resembles that in the preceding case and also resembles most of her efforts at reproducing the forms shown to her. It may require careful analysis to make the assertion convincing that the productions in *Plate 7* are actual efforts to reproduce the figures seen in *Plate 1*. Most of them are composed of small looped units perseverated in a horizontal line, each one varying slightly in form from the previous one in such a way that there is a gradual departure from the simple looped form for a while, and then the variation reverses itself and returns to the

simple form again. Figures 1, 2 and 3 are made up in this way of a perseveration of the horizontal plane in the vertical direction without regard
to gestalt. In Fig. 1 there is no tendency to pairing. The dots become
loops and even the horizontal plane is perseverated. Figure 2 is similar.
In this patient the tendency to perseverate did not carry beyond the
third line. Others of a similar age level would perseverate in both directions until they had covered the paper. Even Fig. 3 is reproduced in the
same way without regard to the gestalt principle involved in it. There
are three horizontal lines of loops, with the middle ones a little longer
than the others. Figure 4 may not seem to resemble the form offered.
The reproduction is much smaller, more nearly conforming with the
units of the other figures, but departs from the other reproductions
enough so that the middle part of it somewhat resembles the form given.
Still, it is not reproduced according to the gestalt principles, because,
although the three-sided figure is fairly complete and there is finally a
form at the lower right hand corner, these two parts were not made
separately in the way that will be shown in the higher mental levels, then
there are perseverations of loops on either side. Figure 5 seems to resemble
even less closely the test form, but there is some apparent effort to en-
large the curved forms and to make an upward stroke, although again not
in a separate way that would indicate the gestalt organization of the
figure. Figure 6 shows clearly the effort to make a continuous sinusoidal
line, with at least three efforts at crossing. But there is also a fragmentation of the figure. This may be a tendency carried over from the former
figures which were made of the looped units. This tendency to carry over
a part or a whole of a former drawing into the next object offered is a
tendency recognized in children (Ament). But fragmentation of perceived form has also been recognized as a common tendency in optic
imagery by Kanner and Schilder and in sensory perception by Schilder
and Bromberg. In Fig. 7 can be seen a crude effort to make two upright
rectangular forms that are separated from each other, are parallel, are
not slanted and do not cross. These difficulties in crossing and slanting
will be discussed again where it is more clearly illustrated. In Figs. 7
and 8 are seen the only evidences of gestalt produced by this patient,
and here, indeed, they are actually exaggerated. Thus, already one may
begin to believe that there are different kinds of gestalten that are perceived or reproduced at different mental levels. Figures 9 and 10 (not
shown) were made by the patient by a perseveration of the looped form
such as in Figs. 1 to 6, but with no apparent resemblance to the test
forms.

A reconsideration of *Plate 7* will now show that the horizontal lines are never straight, but in themselves show a rotational or vertical direction. In subsequent cases it will also be seen that they are never parallel, but always radiate toward or away from each other so that the directional movement as expressed by perseveration is radial. Thus, vertical, directional, radial and wave movement in some way seems to be the basis of the primitively reproduced visual motor pattern.

From this, one may obtain the following corollaries: fixed points are not reproduced as such, but as looped forms, and a straight line is not reproduced as a function of two fixed points, but as a function of a radial directional wave movement. Therefore, parallel lines, angulated forms and crossed forms present great difficulties.

Many similar phenomena have been found in young children. Baldwin followed the course of his child in her ability to draw and copy from the nineteenth to the twenty-seventh month. At the earliest age there was "the simplest and vaguest and most general imitation of the teacher's movements, not the tracing of the mental picture. There was no resemblance of conformity between the child's drawing and the copy. She could not identify it herself." He found that at the earliest age (19 months) there were only sweeping whole arm movements from the shoulder. A few months later, she began to flex the elbow and wrist, and at 27 months she was able to manipulate the fingers. At that time her productions were made of loops in the clock-wise direction, with an emphasis on the horizontal plane. It was also brought out that in each new drawing there was a tendency to carry over a whole or a part of the previous drawing. In this one sees how important in the young child are the motor elements, and in fact it appears that the motor and perceptive elements are dissociated. Similar points were made by Prinzhorn already quoted, and by Ament, who found that at 3 years there was no thought of resemblance between the child's drawing and the model, but that the child seemed to draw from memory (sic?) and not from nature even when the object was before it.

In the Merrill-Palmer intelligence test for pre-school children, copying a circle is the accomplishment of a 3 year old child, copying a cross that of a 4 year old and copying a star that of a 5 year old; in the Stanford-Binet test it is determined that a normal 4 year old child can copy a square, whereas a 7 year old child can copy a diamond.

Movement, fragmentation and curving of forms were shown in the normal optic imagery by Kanner and Schilder, and also difficulties with crossed and angle forms in cutaneous sensory imagery by Schilder and

Bromberg. Also Stein and von Weizsäcker showed that in the pathologic disintegration of sensory phenomena it often happened that a circle or an arc was perceived instead of a cross. Stengel showed in similar types of disturbances that in general there was a tendency to experience a sort of crooked or bent line instead of a straight one. Von Weizsäcker also found in optic disturbances that crossed lines or lines forming acute angles were perceived as parallel lines.

A person with a mental age of 3 years (*Plate 8*) shows many of the same

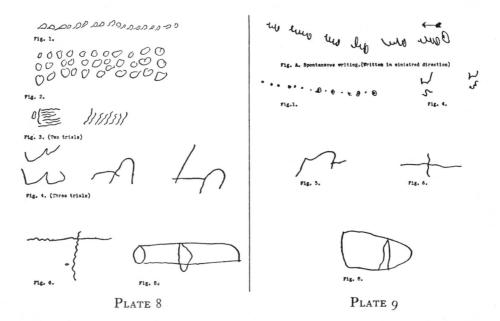

Fig. 1.

Fig. 2.

Fig. 3. (Two trials)

Fig. 4. (Three trials)

Fig. 6.　　Fig. 8.

PLATE 8

Fig. A. Spontaneous writing. (Written in sinistrad direction)

Fig. 1.　　Fig. 4.

Fig. 5.　　Fig. 6.

Fig. 6.

PLATE 9

principles but some additional accomplishments. Figure 1 is a series of small loops (no pairing), with a tendency to vary the loop formation in such a way as to emphasize the horizontal base. The subject perseverated indefinitely in the dextrad direction, but did not perseverate the horizontal plane. Figure 2 is still produced in horizontal lines, and there is some suggestion of vertical planes, but no slanting; thus there is no regard for gestalten in either of these. Figure 3 was recognized as a problem different from the previous ones, but it proved to be an unsurmountable task. The subject attempted the horizontal and vertical perseverations. However, her second effort may be considered a real representation of the gestalt principles involved. The tendency to reproduce a series of dots in a line has also been seen in Stengel in thalamus disturbances, and by Stein and von Weizsäcker in mescaline poisoning. Figure 4 was tried

four times. It is of interest that the first effort is small and does not deviate much from the unit used, for example, in Fig. 1, and may have
been carried over from the previous figures. However, each effort departs more from this small size. It is also of interest that what is apparently here interpreted as crossed lines was not accomplished without
considerable effort. There is some suggestion here that this figure is seen
in two units, or gestalten, but it is not complete. A simple crossed form
is accomplished in Fig. 6 with a definite suggestion of sinusoidal formation, but it is a right angle and not a slanting crossing. Figure 8 is crude,
but the principles of gestalt are well illustrated. I do not know if it is significant from the consideration of directional determinants that at both
this and the previous level, the left end of this figure is closed.

Plate 9 was reproduced by a woman with a mental rating of 5 years.
She could talk and help with simple work about the ward, such as scrub-
bing. She could not write her name or any other meaningful sign. Her
spontaneous production is seen at the top. It was produced in the sinistrad
direction. This tendency is known to be common among children of this
age as well as among mentally defective persons (Orton, Gordon). In
Fig. 1 there is a tendency for the loops to become dots, but still the loops
predominate. In Fig. 4 the gestalt principle is apparently not only in
evidence but exaggerated. The figure itself was perseverated (there were
several more), and the tendency to make the gestalt units so small may
be an example of micropsia or simply a reproduction by reiteration of the
small units, such as the subject used in Fig. 1. The separation of the two
gestalt units is a tendency that occurs frequently in subsequent cases.
It may itself be an indication of movement in sensorimotor phenomena.
Figures 5, 6 and 7 are crude efforts, but in all the gestalt principles
have been active, though the more elaborated function of the exact relationships of the parts to the whole is neglected.

The copying here reported, of the simple gestalten by feebleminded
persons seems to offer some suggestions about the genetic development
of the visual motor patterns, which are in keeping also with other studies
made on children and in pathologic cases of different sorts. It thus appears that the more primitive sensorimotor patterns are dependent on
the principles of constant motion, which seem to be largely a whirling
movement in a vortex in clock-wise and counter-clock-wise direction, with
an associated radiating directional component and with a tendency to
emphasize horizontal planes. Fixed points are difficult to obtain, and
straight lines are not accomplished as the shortest distance between two
fixed points, but as an expression of the radiating tendencies. Parallel

lines do meet before infinity, and crossed lines and angulated forms present great difficulties. There is always added to the radiating lines and planes, whatever may be its use or expression, the tendency for whirling in clock-wise or counter-clock-wise direction. The first evidence of expressed form, as shown at the second year level, is seen as little units of whirls or loops that are perseverated most freely in the horizontal plan in a dextrad direction. This may be largely a motor expression. In the perseveration of the loops, there is a slight constant variation from one to the next, a part of the time deviating away from the simple loop and then returning to it again. Series of such horizontally produced loops may be reduplicated, not in parallel formation, but always showing radiation and the tendency to curve. Some tendencies for gestalt are seen at the 3 year level. These were rectangular forms either near to each other or inside one another. But some of the gestalt principles are functions of the more highly elaborated perceptional motor capacities and only appear at the higher intellectual levels. Above 3 years, there is the tendency to accentuate the horizontal base line, to control perseveration and to produce wavy lines instead of broken ones for the representation of straight lines, and some effort to cross lines. At the 5 year level, there is a tendency to reduce the primitive loops to points, but this tendency is reversible even at the superior adult level, and there is a tendency to make straighter lines and better recognized gestalten. And at all levels all of the original principles are in evidence and tendencies to revert back to them are always present. Thus, there is always the tendency for dots to become loops, for straight lines to curve a little, for parallel lines to radiate toward or away from each other. Above all, there is always the tendency for sensorimotor patterns to revert back to the more primitive principles and to express movement in some way.

CHAPTER IV

MATURATION IN THE PRIMITIVE CHILD

SOME DATA which appears to give evidence that the evolution of gestalten is a maturation process rather than an educational or imitative one is derived from drawings obtained from native African children. This material was kindly given to me by Doctor H. W. Nissen of Yale University. He secured these drawings in Pastoria, a laboratory of the Pasteur Institute (Paris) situated in French Guinea, Africa. In May 1930 while making some naturistic studies of chimpanzee, he administered ten psychometric tests of the individual type to fifty native negro children of 5 to 13 years of age (the exact age could not be determined and had to be estimated). Among these tests were included the drawings of designs from the army performance tests (*See Plate 10*). Although these designs are not the same as the figures which I have used in my study of visual motor gestalten, they lend themselves to the same

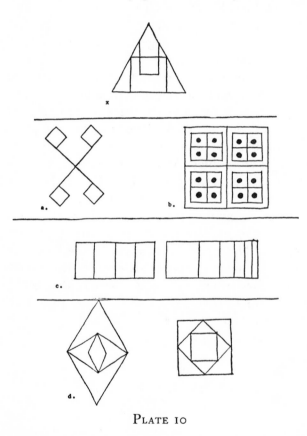

PLATE 10

sort of analysis. In the Army test a standard scoring has been used on adults which allows only two to five possible scores on each design. It will be seen that an analysis of the way in which children reproduce these designs allows a greater range of possible responses. A review and restandardization of these tests on children with this in mind might be justified.

It will be noted that the standard scoring of the drawing of native negro children by Dr. Nissen and his coworkers resulted in no score for many of the children, although an analysis of the drawings showed that in every case the child's drawing showed that the response was directly related to the stimulus.

The term "primitive" child is used here to mean the naive unsophisticated child who has not been subjected to the educational or cultural regime of the child of civilization. It does not assume any difference in native intelligence. The children examined by Dr. Nissen had in some instances (about half) never used paper or pencil before. Nissen, Machover and Kinder in analyzing the results of Dr. Nissen's study have reviewed the whole subject of primitive intelligence. They maintain that there is no available evidence for any clear-cut racial difference in intelligence nor can any conclusions be made concerning general ability or adaptability or primitive native potentialities from any known test materials. However, some test materials do show differences in "specific immediate present abilities". In their own battery of tests they found that the best results were obtained from tests which involve imitative functions, immediate memory, perception and retention of visuo-kinesthetic cues and which were without representative content while the poorests results were obtained from the tests which had pictorially representative content, or symbolic material or which required combinative activity based on the perception of part-whole relationships. The authors felt that from their data no conclusions could be derived as to native endowment. They emphasized, instead, the influence of cultural sets and group phenomena "in conditioning the development of functions with consequent cumulative differentiation" somewhat in the terms of Child's dictum that "Development is a process of functional construction, that is, beginning with a given structure and function the continuance of the function modifies the structural substratum and this in turn modifies further function and so on".

These drawings were made available to me by Dr. Nissen before their analysis was complete. They were analyzed and classified in accordance with the gestalt principles which have been noted in the observation of hundreds of children who have drawn gestalt figures used in this study. Seven levels or stages of accomplishment were distinguished.

I. The first, or most primitive, level. One sees large whole arm scribblings which were produced in such a way as to fill the space allotted without much regard to the form which was presented. The drawings of three children were of this type (*See Plate II of Case 23 of Dr. Nissen's* series). Design X is essentially a meaningless scribble. In design A there appears to have been some effort to use the scribble to form a cross. Design B is essentially a perseveration or carry-over from design A. In design C there is some resemblance to the form given in that one sees a horizontal figure, but again the child's production may have been influenced as much by the space allotted as the form presented except that there is also some suggestion of perseveration of vertical lines on the left-hand side. Design D is essentially a perseveration of design C. Perseverative tendencies are strong and may well be determined by the motor pattern or by kinesthetic clues. This child was said to be left-handed and obviously drew in the sinistrad direction making loops that were both clock-wise and counter-clock-wise. These results represent essentially the simplest form of motor response to the stimuli. There is, however, some slight evidence of responses to the sensory pattern, at least to the extent of adapting the response to the background, which we will recall is the first principle of gestalten (Koffka).

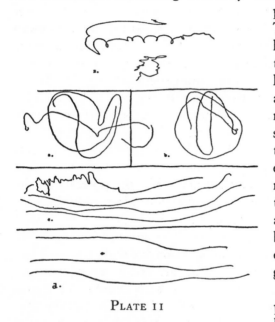

PLATE II

II. In the second level of production there was a good loop formation and the tendency to produce patterns by perseveration of loops in a horizontal place without regard to the form offered but with the apparent intent to fill the space allotted. There was also some evident tendency to put loops inside of loops. Two children produced drawings of this sort. In one instance, in design A, an apparent effort was made to form a cross by crossing the extended arm of an outer loop with a part of the inner loop. The loops otherwise show only perseverative tendencies; they were formed in both the clock-wise and counter-clock-wise direction and perseverated in both the dextrad and sinistrad directions.

III. The first clear evidences of gestalten with an inner structure are seen at this level. They are produced by the spatial relationship of similarly formed loops, and by the perseveration on the horizontal plane of vertical, radial wavy lines. Four children are represented in this group (*See Plate 12*, Case 43). In design X, the child after three trials gives some idea of the original form by means of three inclusive loops. In design A, four loops are properly related to each other but show no connecting crossed lines. Similarly, design B is formed by a grouping of loops. Design C is a simple perseveration of vertical lines. In design D, we again see loops inside of loops.

IV. In the next stage of development we see the relationship drawn between lines and loops and lines to each other. So far, lines have been only segments of loops. Even in design C of *Plate 12*, the lines are probably only small segments of large arcs perseverated in a wave-like manner. The inclusions of such perseverated segments into other loops, or the connection of such a single segment to a loop, or the crossing or angulated relationship of such segments, is a special stage in the development of gestalten. In these primitive levels of development we find the child experimenting with any one of these new combinations but a higher level of development is required for the utilizing of more than one in any design. Thus, in *Plate 13* (Case 28), we see the loops on the ends of the lines but an inability to cross the lines so that the lines remain parallel and horizontal. In design B, there is a square with angles formed by utilizing the lines made on the paper. This child also uses dots. In my experience with children I have found that the utilization of dots rather than small loops represents a higher level of accomplishment. This design also shows the organization of three inclusive different forms and, although the production is crude and not much like the stimulus offered, still it represents a good deal of integration in the gestalten and a recognition of the complexity of the inner structure of the design. In design C again, with the happy use of the material offered and the accentuation of the two most lateral

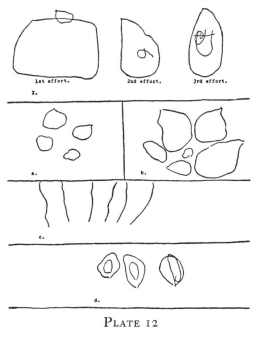

PLATE 12

lines, the child succeeds in getting his perseverated vertical lines inside of a box. His first effort of design D looks suspiciously like a perseveration of design C. Even in his second effort he does not accomplish much, being perhaps confused by his kinesthetic memories and the visual pattern offered.

It is of interest to note that after this analysis was made, comparison with the analysis made by Dr. Nissen and his coworkers of this material showed that they had not been able to give any score to any of these drawings by the standard method, although my analysis shows a definite gradation in performance.

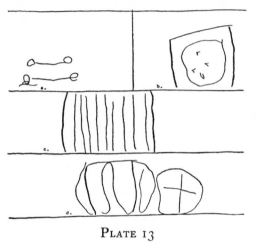

PLATE 13

V. In the more advanced stages we now find either a better utilization of the same elements such as were already illustrated in design B of *Plate 13* or the capacity to utilize several combinations in the same design. This includes the drawings of eight children, all of whom made the lowest possible score by Dr. Nissen and his coworkers. In *Plate 14* (Case 40), we see that design A consists of crossed lines with loops at each end; the lines, however, are vertical, and the loops are on the ends and not at the sides of the lines. Design B is made by four rectangular-like forms more or less correctly related to each other and with an irregular mass and quantity of included material. Design C is more or less correct in form, but at right angles to the proper plane. This was characteristic of five children of this group. Its exact significance is not clear in this setting although in pathological cases the disorientation of a whole figure on its background is a confusional feature. Only one figure is drawn in this design, suggesting that the children do not distinguish any difference between the two patterns and are not impressed by the two figures. Note also that the number of perseverated lines always exceed that of the stimulus which indicates that they represent merely a large number, or many, or plurality. There is no effort to represent the different spatial relationships of the lines. Design D shows an effort to make three inclusive forms with fragmentation which may be the child's best effort at angulation. Slanting and diamond shaped forms are even more difficult than crossed forms.

VI. In the next level we see better produced forms and more accurate relationships. Eleven children produced drawings that fell in this classificatin. In *Plate 15* (Case 41), design C is found in its correct horizontal relationship and there are two separate figures. All of the designs show clearly their resemblance to the test figures.

VII. In the best group of drawings which were obtained from eleven children, all of which received the highest possible score by Dr. Nissen

PLATE 14   PLATE 15

and his coworkers, we see a higher grade of perfection. There is more accuracy in reproducing details and numbers of parts and spatial relationships. In these drawings we note for the first time the ability to make diagonal gestalten with acute and obtuse angles (*See Plate 16*, Case 11).

The best of these productions compare favorably with drawings of the same designs by American negro children of known average intelligence, who were born in New York and educated in the New York schools. This was determined by comparing these drawings with those of fifty American negro children. A number of these drawings of the design A are shown in *Plate 17*. Among the native African children there were found more drawings of the more primitive type, but all levels of maturation are seen in the native African group as well as in the educated American group of children. It will be seen in *Plate 17* of comparable pictures that the drawings of an American child of four are compared with those of one of the African children whose age was estimated at 8 years. In the same way the various recognizable levels of maturation may be found at progressively higher mental level, in the standardized American child and compare with childern of various ages. However, the best, and practically normal, drawing was furnished by an American school girl of eleven and by a native boy of eleven who had had no formal schooling. By way of contrast, the drawing of a child of twelve years who had been in a state hospital since the age of eight years is shown. He was twelve years old at the time of the test and scored a mental age of nine years eleven months. This shows the marked dissociation processes that occur in schizophrenia and which will be discussed in more detail in a subsequent chapter.

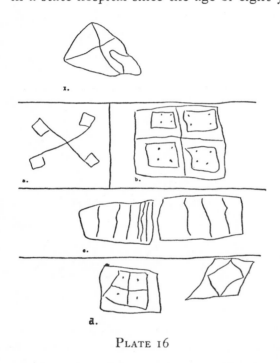

PLATE 16

In conclusion, we may say that a native child who has had no normal education and has had no previous experience with paper and pencil may produce copied forms with the same facility as an average American born and educated child. Among the native children there appears to be a greater range of maturation levels even at the same or similar age levels. They show features which are the same as those that are observed in normal standardized children who are studied at different age levels. It may be noted that copied form evolves as a motor pattern adapted to a given background. The simplest principles of structure depend upon loops which may be perseverated inclusively or on horizontal planes. Lines occur as horizontally perseverated segments of loops in wave-like relationships. More integrated structures are formed by the relationships between such loops and segments of loops into angles and crossed forms. Small loops may become dots, segments represent lines, and angulated forms represent rectangles. Several of these relationships may be utilized at once. Perfection in forms and spatial relationships and accuracy in number of parts (by inhibition of perseveration) are accomplished by some children. The best drawings show slanting forms, non-right angles, alternating and diagonal relationships. The children who produce such sophisticated drawings score the highest on the group of psychometric tests given by Dr. Nissen. The majority of these also include the older children.

The analysis of this material by Dr. Nissen and his coworkers led them to the opinion that the variability of this test was somewhat less than that of the maze test, although the designs seemed to show, to them, a greater discriminative value for the estimated age levels of the group as a whole.

In their analysis of the individual drawings they state: "As will be noted, design A is so constituted as to make possible the detection of a 45-degree rotation appearing in the reproduction. The performance of nearly 50% of our subjects (46% of the younger group and 50% of the older) showed this rotation, the effect being the crossing of a vertical line by a horizontal line instead of the crossing of oblique lines as in the copy. With respect to this feature the design elicited three types of performance: inability to approximate the figure presented; reproduction as a crossing of a horizontal and a vertical line; and reproduction of the diagonal crossing. Performance of the younger group with one exception, was limited to the first two categories. All three categories were present in the performance of the older group but only 17% of the responses of this group came under the first category.

"Design B proved considerably more difficult for our subjects. Whereas in design A there were fifteen zero scores and thirty subjects receiving one point each of a possible three points allowed by the scoring standards, in design B we find thirty-three zero scores and only twelve scores above zero. The highest score was four points (the maximum possible being five points), achieved by a subject of the older group of whom the examiner noted, 'Big, good-natured fellow, the only one who seems at home with the pencil'.

"On design C all but two of the younger group scored zero on both parts, these two each receiving one point, whereas of the older group seven subjects scored on the first part and nine on the second. For design D the scores were zero for all but two of the older group. Like design A, both C1 and C2 showed a certain number of rotations, but here the rotation was through 90°, so that the predominantly horizontal extension appeared as predominantly vertical extension in the reproductions. This rotation appeared less frequently than in the design A (9% of the at-

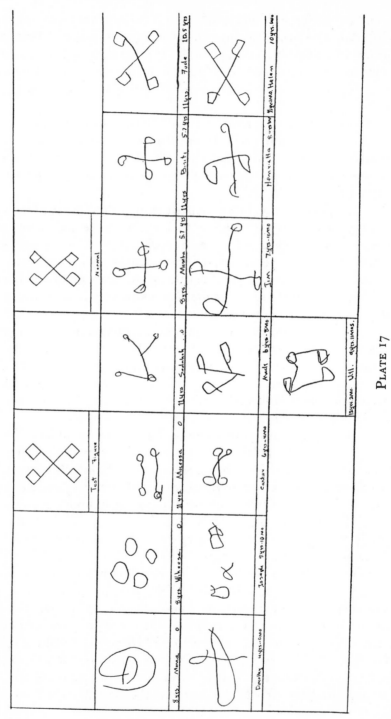

PLATE 17

tempts of the younger group and 21% of the older group). It suggests that for our subjects the extensity of the designs was the more important feature, the direction being secondary. The tendencies to rotation exhibited in the reproductions in design A, C1 and C2 are probably expressive of the ontogenetically prior prepotency of verticality and horizontality over obliqueness, and of verticality over horizontality, of the perceptual organization of, and motor adjustment to, spatial extensity. The priority in development of certain directional tendencies in copying design had been recognized by Gesell and utilized by him in his normative schedule. Tendencies to rotation in the design tests like the reversals in the cube imitation test suggest the general problem of orientation and merit investigation as to whether such phenomena appear as prominently among negro children of comparable age with American upbringing".

The material of this study does investigate this problem and indicates that spatial orientation cannot be spoken of in terms of ontogenesis but in terms of organization of the perceptual motor patterns and that it follows a definite pattern in the different maturation levels which are alike in the so-called primitive and civilized child, except that in the children studied by Dr. Nissen there are more than the primitive patterns.

CHAPTER V

OPTIC IMAGERY AND MOVEMENT AS THE MEANS OF ORGANIZING REPRESENTATION

OPTIC IMAGES have been studied by Kanner and Schilder who conclude that movement is one of the inherent qualities of representation whether by perception or imagery. Similar laws exist for optic perception, after images, eidetic imagery (Urbantschitsch and Jaensch) and optic imagery. Although Kanner and Schilder were mainly concerned with the imagination of rather complicated figures, with movements of parts of the body as well as that of external objects, they also started their experiments with the imagination of simpler figures. Of special interest from the point of view of the present discussion are the results which their subjects obtained when they imagined circles. The first subject says, "The circle begins to revolve clock-wise and goes around in a spiral way, making circles which become wider and wider". A second subject says, "A part of the outline dissolves with little wave-like moments; the change in the circumference is experienced as vivid motion". The fourth subject says, "The radius becomes larger and larger and the circle spreads out in its periphery until it merges into the darkness of the background". On a second effort this subject says, "It gets smaller and smaller and the line darkens until finally nothing is left". A fifth subject "sees a number of concentric circles moving slowly in a counter clock-wise direction". The authors indicate that in this type of simple figure there were two forms of movement, namely: Elementary or primitive movement such as fading, irradiation, scintillation, expansion, contraction and wave-like movements; and movement determined by the form of the figure which would be circular in this figure.

Four subjects were used for the present experiment, two men and two women. They were two artists, a teacher and a nurse. It was found that not all individuals could be used for this experiment as some individuals do not seem to experience optic images, at least not adequately enough to describe them. It was also found that some of the subjects did not limit their experiences to the field of optic images but that the stimulus was used to arouse experiences in other fields: sometimes images were aroused in other perceptual fields such as the auditory field, while one subject was inclined to associate so freely with symbols from conceptional and emotional experiences that it tended to make the experiment less valuable than was desired from the point of view of optic imagery.

The subjects were not acquainted with the nature of the experiment. They were presented with the gestalt figure on separate cards and asked to study them carefully until they had a clear concept of them (usually about one minute) and then the card was taken from them and it was suggested that they close their eyes and try to imagine the object, describe their image of it, to hold the imagination as long as possible and describe what happened to it until finally the optic field was again at rest. Afterwards they were asked to draw a picture of the different images which they experienced. The figures in *Plate 18* are the subjects' own drawings of what they observed.

Figure A, Subject A (Teacher) describes Fig. A by saying the two parts "tend to separate. The circle remains in the same position but tends to get larger and it elongates in the horizontal direction and tends to move to the right; meanwhile the square has disappeared". Subject B (Artist) describes this figure as "A circle and diamond on a background: it gets larger in relation to the background; the circle is more prominent than the square as though it had come in the foreground and seemed to have a thicker oily consistency. Several concentric circles are now formed, the inner smaller ones are receding into the background". The square when asked for had been forgotten. Subject C (Artist) describes "A circle and a square that touch at one point; they move slightly towards and-away from me. Now they form two overlapping circles that make a well known design which Hautpmann used in the Lindbergh kidnapping case. Now it is three interlocked circles which is the trademark for Krupp (he claimed it was a machine gun symbol); now it is five interlocked circles for the five nations of the Olympian games; now it is reduced to one small point. (Square?) I don't even think of it" (*See Plate 18*). Subject D (Nurse) says, "There is a circle with a square, the circle gets larger and the square stays small, and the circle gets larger and larger and overlaps the square until the circle entirely encloses the square and then the square disappears" (*See Plate 18*).

Figure 1. Subject A says, "There is a row of dots in groups of twos or pairs. The space between the groups of twos is larger and the space between the two dots in a pair is smaller. One pair tends to separate from the row and move above the others. They all tend to get larger and smaller again and the line loses its regularity because one pair after another moves out and in again". Subject B says, "There are dots in a line which stay very clear but other dots of lines appear; these are above

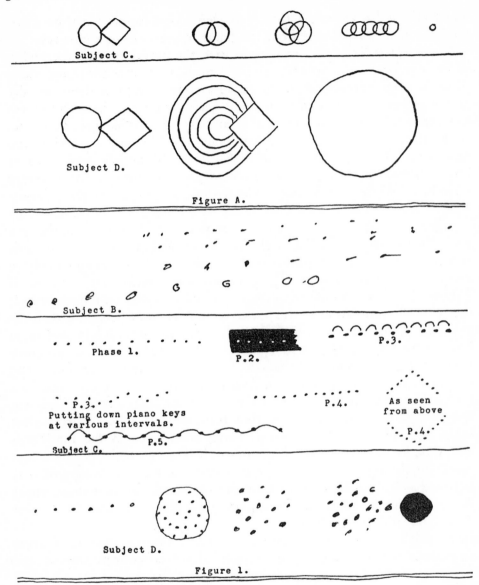

Subject C.

Subject D.

Figure A.

Subject B.

Phase 1.

P.2.

P.3.

P.3.

Putting down piano keys
at various intervals.

P.4.

As seen
from above

P.4.

P.5.

Subject C.

Subject D.

Figure 1.

PLATE 18

and tend to move somewhat to the right and seem to be in the distance, they seem to be pulled out in these three directions as though by extension, they tend to become less distinct in the distance. Then the last line is put exactly above the other as though it were an after-thought" (*See*

Plate 18). Subject C says, "I see twelve black dots on a white background. If the color was reversed, that is if there were twelve white dots on a black background they would appear like six pairs of eyes. The dots suggest to me a jumping movement so that I have to jump from one dot to the next one to the right. They seem to be the keys of a piano so that when you push them down you get music. Now I imagine them in different depths so that some are near me and some farther away and they form a rectangle on a horizontal plane, but I cannot see this since they are in the same plane; I only imagine it. Now there are imaginary semi-circle connections between each two dots like a physicist's diagram of tones. Now there is so much movement in it you can imagine it like a sleigh-ride running downhill". Subject D reports, "there are dots in a straight line and all moving up and down, back and forth and around until they move into a cell-like circle formation. There is no outline to the circle; I don't know what makes them stay in the circle; they are all moving about all the time but they can't get out".

Figure 2, *Plate 19*. Subject A says, "This is an intricate design but it does not hold its shape. At first there is a series of little circles in three slanting from left to right. But the position of the circles tends to change. In the first series of three circles at the left, the two above separate from the one below which is directly below and gets larger. Now the original design is entirely lost and there are three parallel lines but not directly under each other; now it is just one line slanting down and now the line multiplies and they are not parallel but would all tend to meet if they were continued. There are no circles at all". Subject B says, "There is lots of fast motion in the design. First there are a series of three dots slanting down and to the right, then there is a series slanting from the left, then both are there making a series of crosses but they are not dots any more but just lines, now some of the crosses at the right have taken on circles; now all of the crosses have blossomed into a row of circles and all of the circles move around and make a round frame". Subject C says, "There are rows of three circles arranged in a vertical way but it is very difficult to keep any impression because there is a restless movement. I feel as if something was unsatisfactory about it. They might be soldiers' heads which are in formation; they are supposed to look to the left but they turn and look at me, although I don't see their faces, only the tops of their heads as though from above. Now instead of keeping in vertical rows of three they seem to jump into two long vertical rows but there is not enough space; they try to arrange in every possible way, also in two or one long horizontal line, but they are not supposed to be that way or

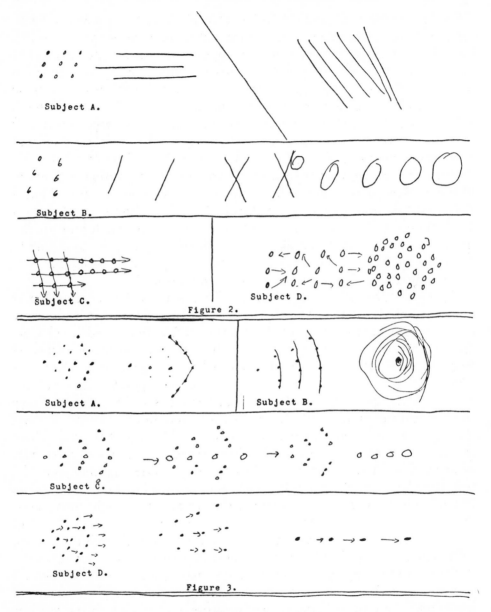

Subject A.

Subject B.

Subject C.

Subject D.

Figure 2.

Subject A.

Subject B.

Subject C.

Subject D.

Figure 3.

PLATE 19

else there is not enough room and they try to rearrange back in the original way. They are like molecules or atoms that jump around and don't have enough space". Subject D says, "There are little ovals in threes; at first they move up and down, three together in the direction of the slanting, then they get faster and faster and move back and forth from one row to the next and suddenly jump out of line by their own initiative and form a circular mass".

Figure 3. Subject A says, "There is a design of dots with one large dot and three to the right of it and five more to the right, etc.; these are in angular formation. The figure stays the same shape but everything gets larger, the dots get larger and the space between them gets larger. The large single dot in the middle (Note) stays still and the others move away to the right. Now the row in the center and the most distant one becomes most distinct and the others fade so that it looks like an arrow pointing to the right". Subject B says, "It is like a fan. There are four rows of dots with one lone one and the others form slightly curved arcs. It seems that the design is made from the one lone dot, it increases, blossoms out. It might be like part of a funnel, like a drop of water that splashes in water and forms circles in the water that tend to engulf themselves". Subject C says, "They are dots arranged in series of one, three, five and seven; the last three are in angle formation of more than 90°. At first you might imagine that it was like a Christmas tree lying on its side. Then it is like something that is being pushed from left to right with such force that the ends are being bent backwards. The middle dots are moving faster than the other ones and tend to leave them behind; finally the middle line would move entirely away leaving the others in the air. I try to imagine moving from right to left but imagination fails me. Now I can imagine the whole thing as a kite that moves away to the right in the wind, but it turns on the axis of the dot 45° and moves up. Now the inside dots have disappeared and only the rhomboid outline can be seen". Subject D says, "There were four rows of dots in half circles. They seemed to move out to the right, except the single one which always stayed still; it is as though the whole thing stretched to the right, then it would come back again but every time it stretched out and came back it lost one of the dots on the outside of the design so finally there was only the middle row left, stretching to the right from the point of the first dot and coming back again".

Figure 4, *Plate 20*. Subject A says, "The two parts of the figure become separated. The top of the curved part stretches back towards the square. The square becomes a completely closed square and the curved part disappears". Subject B says, "The line of the square box, where it is near the hat shape gets heavier and tends to engulf the hat. The lines tend to become parallel. Another line crosses at the same point and the whole thing becomes like an intricate design. The ends of the hat design curl up into circles. Now there is a tendency for numerous complicated designs to form, it is hard to grasp any one but finally a circle forms right in the box and another one in the hat". Subject C says, "I see a square with a wavy line but it gives me an uneasy feeling because it is unbalanced; the square will fall down, but it turns at an angle of 45° and the wavy line is balanced on the tip of the square like something on the nose of a seal; now it turns further and the square is resting squarely on the top of the wave and gradually sinks into it; now the wave tends to expand and contract and the two ends come together and cannot separate. Now the whole thing is in one enclosed figure". Subject D says, "The square seems to get smaller and larger, the missing line is drawn in and the

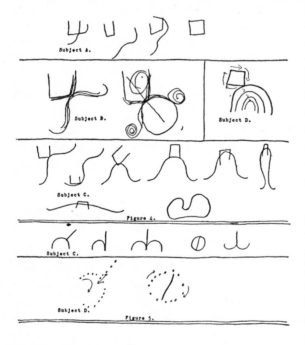

PLATE 20

square whirls around in a clock-wise direction. The curved part became a simple half circle and got larger and smaller together with the square. None of them became smaller than actual size; everything tends to get larger and then return to normal size".

Figure 5. Subject A says, "The figure has come too close at the bottom in a point. The line at the top has become longer; the dots are larger. The figure is now more nearly a circle although there is a suggestion of a point at the bottom but it continues to become less of a point and more of a circle. I don't notice the line at the top any more; it is nearly a perfect circle made of a continuous line not of dots. At the point where the line touches the arc another line appears, now two half circles meet at that point, many other points of light start to develop at that point but nothing comes of them; everything seems to happen at that point. The dots tend to coalesce into a continuous line but this is definitely accomplished only at the point where they touch". Subject C says, "The dots immediately form into continuous lines. The straight line is unsatisfactory because of the angle it forms with the circle. It moves down the side of the circle and aligns itself along the side (tangent) of the round circle and the circle turns around and I see two half circles with this line between. Then the two half circles turn around and form a circle with the line as the diameter of the circle but then it returns to the other position of two half circles and this line standing perpendicular between them". Subject D says, "There is a half circle of dots, it forms into a circle. The line of dots going up from the circle moves down into the circle and back up in its original position again. It gets longer and shorter. When it is shorter the dots make a compact line, when it stretches out the dots separate again. It comes together quick but spreads out and separates the dots slower. The circle is going round and round in a clock-wise direction. The straight line is all inside now but does not go around with the circle but stays in the same slanting position; it is a solid line while the circle is still made of dots."

Figure 6, *Plate 21*. Subject A says, "The ends of the horizontal line tend to go down; the vertical lines seem to move to the right, both lines tend to flatten out, now they do not seem to cross at all and it is hard for me to visualize it." Subject B says, "They are curly lines that cross; if I were drunk they would look like snakes; more curly

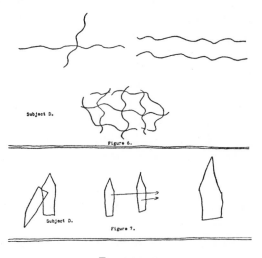

PLATE 21

lines form at the point of crossing but they are fainter and others form nearer the end of the horizontal one, making it look like an insect with legs. Now one of the fainter curly lines is in the form of a half circle or moon. I feel as if I had been influenced by the previous forms, as if I had retained an impression and was using it now. A series of circles form now at the point where the lines cross and move along towards the head of the thing (to the right)". Subject D says, "It started with two moving lines; they move about and separate and become parallel, then many more form like them and are all mingling together, in amongst each other like a ball or a circle; finally there is no clear crossing at all that I can see although there should be if there are so many mingling."

Figure 7. Subject A says, "The two figures lengthen, the two lines coming to a point become longer than the sides and get longer and longer. Now instead of two figures there is only one. The right one disappeared. The one that is left lengthened out and is very long". Subject B says, "The lower torpedo shoots off and extends itself into a series of longer points. Also the second torpedo extends out in the black bottom in the way that cartoonists indicate speed". Subject D says, "First there is one figure attached to another, then they separate, and then they are both sitting up at the same angle. Then there is just one. The one on the left moves into the right and it becomes bigger and then smaller again but still larger than either one alone. The long peak elongates".

Figure 8. Subject A says, "The diamond in the middle has become very long and has widened the figure. The figure has lost its points and has become two parallel horizontal lines not closed at the end and these seem to get longer indefinitely". Subject B says, "The entire thing dances or shimmers due to the diamond in the center throwing off replicas which tend to close up, then the entire design throws off images, now it resembles a revolving cylinder upon which the light has been reflected which creates duplicate images of the cylinder and a lot of action". Subject D says, "Both the long thing and the little diamond in the middle get larger and smaller together but nothing else happens".

It is remarkable that these few adults in a few minutes of consciously experiencing their optic images, re-experience all the processes which the children show in different maturation periods. There is a certain amount of variation in these four different adults, but practically every principle is demonstrated.

In Fig. A, the circle is by all odds the important figure; it enlarges or multiplies itself and engulfs the square, or the square is forgotten. The square on the right apparently suggested the principle of dextrad direction by causing the circle to elongate itself or duplicate itself in that direction. Movement is by expansion and contraction with the center of the circle fixed, or it is circular, clock-wise.

In Fig. 1, the dots exaggerate the tendency for molecular movement; this may occur in pairs in the subject that recognized the pairs, in the dextrad direction, by duplication of the lines in three dimensions, or by forming a circle and, finally, a solid ball.

Figure 2 proves to be a problem to the subjects. They all complain that it is a restless or unsatisfactory design. It will be recalled that Wertheimer used this design to prove that proximity of parts might overcome what would otherwise be considered the natural configuration so that in this design the three vertically slanting loops rather than the horizontal lines, stand together. In small children, however, the horizontal lines are perceived as gestalt by preference and in the optic images these subjects report a struggle between the two tendencies. The first subject starts with the vertically slanting formation, shifts to the horizontal and finally settles on a configuration that is a sort of compromise; the second subject quickly reaches a satisfactory compromise by having crosses of vertical lines slanting in both directions and those are replaced by horizontal rows of the primitive circle. The third subject shifts back and froth between the two until a formless mass results, struggles hopelessly in both directions. The fourth observer solves the problem quickly by jumbling together all the little bodies in a primitive circular mass.

In Fig. 3, the subjects recognize that this, too, is an intricate design by tending to see it at one time or another merely as an outlined figure on a background such as a kite, or a fan, or a Christmas tree. In all cases the single dot is looked upon as the "center" or fixed point of the figure. The term "center" is used even by those subjects who do not consciously describe the design as a segment of a circle, although one observer did visualize it as a possible funnel or a drop of water splashing in water and making circles that tend to engulf one another. The other observers tended to emphasize the dextrad directional feature of the design due to the horizontal features in the design, especially of the middle line which is determined by the single dot. The design tends to expand and contract in relation to this dot and usually to lose the other parts of the design, with the exception of the middle horizontal row.

Figure 4 is experienced in a somewhat different way by each observer, but the ultimate outcome is for each at least one enclosed figure. Some of the subjects experiment in many unsatisfactory ways until they at last reach a solution of the problem. They complain that it is not balanced, that parts of it will fall down, that it moves about and cannot come to rest until they finally reduce it to a simple closed figure. The second observer (subject B) does not obtain such a simple figure but a rather elaborate design which includes several enclosed circles surrounding the point of contact between the two figures and which becomes very much reenforced in the representation; this reenforcement apparently brings the figure to rest about a point of fixation. This same phenomena also is experienced by him in the next figure.

Figure 5 is quickly formed into a complete circle with the upper line coming into a more natural relation to the circle either by becoming its diameter or its tangent. Again, subject B tends to form a re-enforced point of fixation at the point of contact between the line and the half circle and therefore his figures do not become enclosed but duplicate themselves. Subject C wavers back and forth between a similar experience and the closed configuration.

In Fig. 6, the difficulty with the crossing is expressed in different ways by the different observers. Subject A slides the vertical line off the right end of the horizontal as the two become flatter and fainter; subject B again uses the point of crossing as a fixation point but cannot come to rest in this way and instead forms little circles which roll off the right end of the figure; subject D frankly separates the two and then rolls up many wavy lines in a ball so fast that the point of crossing can never be observed.

In Fig. 7 the slanting relationship of the two figures tends to straighten itself and the figures separate and then coalesce into one. The long points are an indication for further elongation. They represent a vector or direction.

In Fig. 8, the relationships are fairly stable, the long points on the little inner diamond suggest elongation of this figure and, therefore, expansion of its surrounding figure. The two long points on the end of the larger figure suggest the indefinite elongation of two parallel lines.

In summary then, we come to the following conclusion: that the inherent quality of all optic images is movement. This movement is based on the elementary movements of whirling, waving, expansion, contraction, scintillation, molecular movement, etc. The simplest form is an enclosed circle which has a fixed center but no fixed periphery. A point is the center of a possible circle. A line is a direction and the most primitive direction is horizontal dextrad. All configurations tend to make use of some of the elementary forms of movement in order to realign themselves into a primitive quiescent form.

Individual variations among subjects may be noted. Subject A tended to cling to the offered design and resist the biological drives as much as possible and often reached some sort of compromise. Subject B showed a facile and excessive experimentation with the figures, complaining at the time that they were unsatisfactory or restless; he also brought into play elaboration and associations from other fields, and there was a certain amount of conscious satisfaction when a solution was reached. Subject C showed certain individual tendencies in bringing an elaborate, often unbalanced and open design to rest by re-enforcing a point of fixation; this subject is a professional graphic artist. The fourth subject (D) was most naive and quickly brought her figures to the most primitive configuration. She seemed to be strongly eidetic.

CHAPTER VI

TACHISTOSCOPIC PHENOMENA AND
THE TEMPORAL FACTOR

GOLDSTEIN, Poppelreuter and Pötzl have used the tachistoscope to demonstrate. agnostic disturbances which otherwise do not appear distinctly. Matthaei has suggested that the genesis of gestalten could be studied under conditions in which the outward stimulus was reduced to the minimum of the short time exposure of the tachistoscope. Lindeman refers to the eidotropic (G. E. Mueller) changes which occur with tachistoscopic exposure because the perceived form is less objective and more in accordance with the biological laws of the optic field. Schilder and Ross showed incomplete figures tachistoscopically and demonstrated that they were completed according to the wishes of the subject. Schilder comments that the tachistoscopic world is a more primitive world and that by this method the origin of primitive form can be studied.

I have attempted to study the laws of the gestalt function by the tachistoscopic exposure of the gestalten to a number of adults, doctors, nurses, medical students, etc. The time of exposure was the least possible to enable the individual to report some form of perception. The results of the experiments confirms in many ways the principle of the genesis of the visual motor gestalten which have already been demonstrated in the drawings of children.

Figure A was variously reported as two circles joining or not joining, or the right hand figure was reported to be more or less like a square (*See Plate 22*).

Figure 1 was usually seen as a dextrad horizontal series of dots or small loops; one observer reported that the line was duplicated and on the second trial that it was triplicated, but this observer was exposed to Fig. 2 before Fig. 1.

Figure 2 was reported by a number of observers as two, three, four or five parallel rows of dextrad, horizontal series of small loops, so arranged that each underlying line was shifted a little to the dextrad direction thus forming a slanting design (*See Plate 22*). However, when given more time to perceive the figure they reported that they immediately experienced it as horizontal dextrad rows of slanting series of three loops. One realizes from this experiment that the surprising observation that a mature individual actually perceives this design differently from a child under

47

the age of six is a problem in the more intricate organization of the material. The first principle is the dextrad horizontal direction, which, at the most primitive level, is perceived one row at a time and, at the more mature level, the whole design is perceived as a dextrad horizontal directional series of three small loops slanting in a vertical direction. This may give us some insight into the reason why children in viewing a complicated picture see parts and not the whole picture, which gives the impression of contradicting the established rules of gestalt. This would suggest the significance of the temporal factor in the gestalt function which in the mature adult is fully integrated into the gestalt function. But in the adult if the temporal factor is reduced to the minimum, there is a tendency to reversion to the primitive reaction. Thus time is the first factor in maturation and it seems actually to become integrated into the individual's capacity to experience things. We find, therefore, that in the gestalt problem of reproducing perceived form the factors that contribute to the integration are: (1) The biological character of the visual field or the principles of perception based upon spatial relationships; (2) Temporal relationships based upon the span of the preceding experiences of the individual and, therefore, upon the length of the maturation process; (3) Motility factors which are closely related in the impulses and attitudes towards the problem itself. In general it may be said that the greater the expanse of the experience that has preceded the immediate act, the more intricate is the temporal factor integrated into the totally experienced pattern. It, therefore, happens that the adult under ordinary circumstances perceives Fig. 2 as a dextrad horizontal series of a group of three vertically slanting loops, while the child perceives it as a series of dextrad horizontal series of loops recurring in a parallel series one below the other an indefinite number of times; and an adult who is obliged to perceive the pattern with an inadequate amount of time experiences it in the same way.

Figure 3 is often reported verbally, "a bunch of dots; I can hardly tell how they were". Then, on a second trial or with a slightly longer time exposure, they are reported to be in the form of a dextrad, horizontal sequence of arcs (*See Plate 22*) or as a segment of concentric circles starting with a dot on the left side; and they are reproduced in this way. There is uncertainty as to the actual number of arcs; there may be reported three, four or five. Some observers have reported that there was a dextrad horizontal series of a more or less parallel vertical lines composed of an uncertain number of dots (*See Plate 22*). This experiment is influenced by the immediately preceding Fig. 2. Ross and Schilder have shown how in the tachistoscopic exposure of human figures, the perception of one figure may be influenced by the previous one even when the preceding figure was not fully reproduced or described, but when the subject had the feeling that they had seen more than they could recall. This is another point which suggests that the actual time element of perception is an important element in the "gestaltung" of the experience. This also, of course, re-emphasizes the tendency for all gestalten to be organized in the form of closed circular patterns which is apparently a fundamentally biological characteristic of the visual field.

Figure 4 is observed and reproduced as two partially closed figures near to each other; often they do not touch, and often the slanting relationship is not observed. The emphasis is usually made upon the square form of the upper figure while the lower one may be represented as a wavy line. This, too, seems to be due to the short time of the exposure which permits of the clear perception of the first figure since the sinistrad figure is always the first figure.

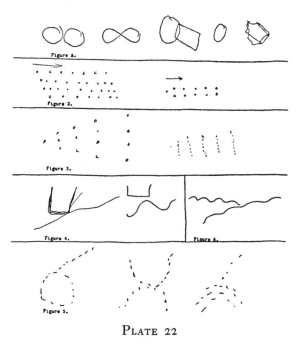

PLATE 22

Figure 5 is variously experienced as a nearly or entirely closed loop with a dash at the top; or as two partially closed loops; or as a series of loops with one dash (*See Plate 22*). This shows clearly that arcs tend to become completely closed circles and that a segment of an arc tends to bring out in the visual field the experience of the vortex or circular forms. Ross and Schilder have also shown that in the exposure of incomplete human figures the observers tend to perceive completed figures.

Figure 6 demonstrates the difficulties in crossing lines. Several observers denied that the lines were crossed even when specifically asked (*See Plate 22*); and many expressed an uncertainty.

Figure 7 was usually interpreted as two angular figures with four to six sides which had a horizontal dextrad relationship. There was often uncertainty as to whether they touched, overlapped, or were separated, and whether the relationship was a parallel or slanting one. Sometimes one figure, usually the first or sinistrad one, was larger than the other.

Figure 8 was naively perceived as a closed figure elongated on the horizontal plane with a small closed figure in its center. Sometimes, however, it was perceived as two overlapping closed figures in the dextrad horizontal direction, which, interestingly enough, was the manner in which it was originally constructed by Wertheimer, who, however, recognized that the continuation of the horizontal lines would tend to dominate the composition.

We observe from these experiments that many primitive features are revealed in the visual motor gestalt experience by limiting the time element. This seems to indicate that the temporal factor is important in the more mature experience. It is as though in each new act of perception, in a small but measurable unit of time, an individual re-experienced the whole maturation process of that sensory field and by so experiencing it integrates it into the pattern. It is not enough, therefore, that there be a pattern in the external physical world which represents a given pattern and a receptive visual field which is receptive just because there is a constant motion in it which enables any pattern to fit into the matrix, but there must in addition be time for the pattern and the motile field to align themselves into a harmonious agreement; and the ability for the motile field to align itself in agreement with the pattern depends upon the period of maturation.

A girl (V. G.) of inferior but not defective intelligence, yet with a constitutional personality defect of the infantile hysterical type was presented the figures first with the tachistoscope and then in the usual way. Her reproductions are shown in *Plates 23* and *24*. We see how much more primitive the tachistoscopic experiences are than those in which she was allowed sufficient time. But, even at the best, her gestalt productions are infantile. With the tachistoscope there is a tendency to separate parts that belong together, as in Figs. A, 4 and 7. The organization of Fig. 3 is in terms of parallel lines of dots; the figure drawn probably represents little more than the observer's uncertainty as to the formation of the mass of dots. The difficulty in crossing is seen in Fig. 6 and the tendency to perseverate from one figure to the next is shown in Figs. 7 and 8.

In summary, it seems that the use of a short time exposure of the forms by the tachistoscope leads to the experiencing of more primitive forms which suggests that the temporal factor is important in total experience, and that the active relationship that exists between the observer and the stimulus, and which creates the visual motor gestalt or experience, requires an actual time unit for the creation, and that this temporal factor moreover results in a different type of gestalt experience. If the time is insufficient, the pattern epxerienced is similar to that observed by a small child (as in Fig. 2). It seems, therefore, that one important factor in the maturation of visual motor patterns is the integration of the tem-

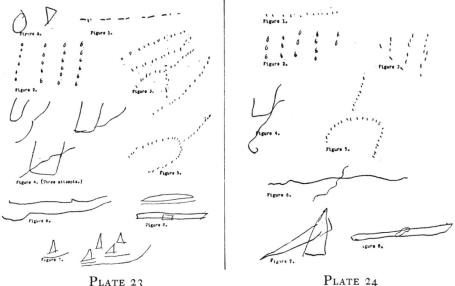

PLATE 23   PLATE 24

poral factor into the whole situation and that this is not separable from the total pattern without resulting in a more primitive reaction. If one wants to become philosophical, one might conjecture that the capacity to integrate the temporal factor into immediately created perception requires a certain life span of experience. In auditory patterns such as tunes, the temporal factor is more obvious and the capacity to perceive or create such patterns with immediacy as composers can, represents a mature type of ability. The concept of maturity rightfully carries with it the idea of ripening with time.

The time factor is never lacking in the visual motor gestalt function. In the young child it can be observed as though it were more conscious; at least the observer of the child may be made conscious of it. The child sees first one row and then another row and then another row in a predetermined sequence. The predetermined sequence is determined bio-

logically and by the laws of gestalt. In the adult this happens unconsciously in a period of time so short that it seems to be instantaneous, but
sufficiently long that if a shorter period is allowed the perception is interrupted in an incomplete or immature stage of integration.

Another way in which the time factor in its relation to gestalten can be
studied is by determining the effect of the lapse of time upon experienced
gestalten either by memory or by constant repetition of the visual motor
pattern. The recall of the figure after a lapse of time also tends to reduce

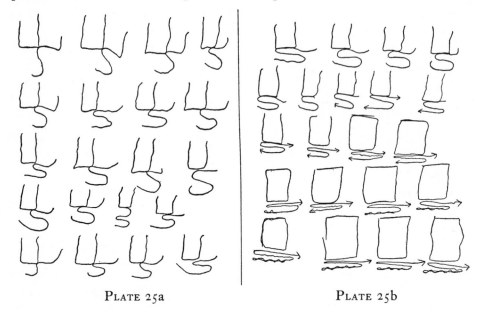

PLATE 25a   PLATE 25b

the figure to the most enclosed, conservative and well-balanced configuration. A visiting physician was asked to draw the figures one day and
two days later without warning was asked if he could reproduce them
from memory. He recalled Fig. A in such a way that the right-hand figure
was a square and not in the diamond orientation. He thought that the
crossing in Fig. 6 was at right angles. He recalled Fig. 8 correctly but
could not recall any other figures. A normal child of eleven years drew
the figure one day and, finding that the physician was pleased, tried to
win praise three days later by redrawing the same figure from memory.
Figure A was reproduced so that a square was inside of a circle; Fig. 5
was recalled so that it was a dotted circle with a dash vertically upward.
A physician associated with the author, and who was much interested
in the gestalt experiments and experimented with the figures himself for
some time, later dropped the interest for several weeks. When he at-

tempted to draw Fig. 4 on the blackboard in staff conference, he drew it so that it was a closed square.

Curran and Schilder have made some studies in memory by asking subjects to retell the same story as often as they were willing to do so and, also, to redraw the gestalt figures as often as they could be persuaded to do so. *Plates 25a* and *25b* show the drawing of Fig. 4 by a patient—with a Korsakoff syndrome. This individual, of course, had a gross disturbance in his memory—but similar phenomena were found among normal individuals, except that in cases of Korsakoff disorders the tendency to reduce the configuration to its simplest and most primitive terms occurred in a shorter period of time. This shows that a configuration repeatedly experienced tends to revert to the primitive structure as determined by the biological laws of the functioning organism, rather than by the original stimulating pattern. Wulf and Koffka have shown that memory traces are determined by these principles of simplification and balancing of remembered figures. Schilder and Curran discuss the problem of memory by repetition and Schilder, in a book now in press, takes up the more general problem. He defines the memory difficulties in Korsakoff cases as exaggerated forgetting and he shows that memories are pale, simplified, primitive, balanced images of the original experience.

The first principle of perception is the motility that is present usually in whirls of the visual field, which, in itself, assumes time; the second principle is direction, usually horizontal and dextrad, which assumes time; the third is mass which is two dimensional direction, and which assumes time. Actual forms arise from these by inhibition of the movement of whirling into closed circles or segments of circles; of the direction into a line; and of the mass into form on a background. Inhibition means taking a unit of time. The complexity of the pattern experienced depends on the capacity for immediate perception of different units in accordance with the principles laid down by the perceptual and motor patterns. It is determined by the maturation level.

Finally we may say, therefore, that the factors which determine the gestalt are:

1. The stimulating pattern in the physical world which also must obey certain laws of gestalt.
2. The motility of the visual field which determines spatial relationships.
3. The temporal factor determined by the motility and sequential relationships which tend to become more intricately integrated

into the spatial relationships with maturation processes and are determined, therefore, by the temporal factor of the life span of the individual.

4. The motor reaction pattern of the individual, his attitudes towards and actual participation in the individually created experience.

5. The immediate tendency for each of these factors to be non-separable from the others.

PART II. CLINICAL CONSIDERATIONS

CHAPTER VII

SENSORY APHASIA AND THE CEREBRAL LOCALIZATION OF THE VISUAL MOTOR GESTALT FUNCTION*

CLASSICAL NEUROLOGY and the association school of psychology teach that the function of nerve tissue is the reception of sensory stimuli by sensory endings and the propagation of the resulting impulse, presumably unmodified, over the nerve fiber to the motor or other efferent organ. Sherrington emphasized the integrative action of the nervous system as a function of the reflex arc, with plurireceptive summation and interference through the synapses converging on the final common path. In some way, however, he recognized that the threshold of the sensory ending may form patterns by selection of modes of stimuli, and he recognized patterns of integrated reactions, accounting for purposeful responses. Lashley, more in sympathy with the recent gestalt teachings, attributed to the final common path the capacity to be sensitized to spatial and temporal patterns which arise from excitations in the sensory endings as a characteristic of integrated behavior. Psychologic data, according to the association school of psychology, are said to arise from simple sensory impressions which are secondarily organized, by combination in the various centers or groups of synapses of the central nervous system, into a mosaic to which meaning is added by association to give experience of the world as one knows it. Gestalt psychology, however, has brought evidence to show that organized units or configurations or gestalten are the units of psychologic data, and that their perception and integration are the primary function of the nervous system at every level, including the first sensory level. According to Köhler, the sensory field is organized by the relative properties of the stimulation through a process of dynamic self-distribution in the stimulating field into functional wholes which precede their parts. He contended that the "mutual relatedness" of qualities is a primary fact of perception. "All experienced order in space is a true representation of a corresponding order in the underlying dynamical context of physiological processes". Structuralization is thus a psychophysical process, physiologically determined. Koffka also said that the physiologic process is structural. "Structures, then (gestalten),

* From the Arch. of Neur. & Psych. Sept. 1933, 30; 514–537.

are very elementary reactons which phenomenally are not composed of constituent elements; their members being what they are by virtue of . . . . their place in the whole". Schilder went beyond the Berlin school with their doctrine of gestalt function fixed and established as a physiologic process at the perceptive level; he claimed that the gestalt which is already present in sensation builds itself up more and more in the nervous system. "There is not only a shape but a shaping".

The higher centers of the cerebrum probably serve as centers of more intricate types of organization, with a tendency to localization of function about the specialized sensory fields. So far, organization or structuralization in the cortical sensory fields has been the main subject of interest in the gestalten studied. That lower centers, such as those of the spinal cord and peripheral nerves, also deal with totally integrated material has been shown by Bromberg and Schilder and by Bromberg in tactile sensibility. It has also been shown by Schilder and myself that lesions in the peripheral nerves and spinal cord will cause disturbances in the gestalt function of this field.

The problem of this study is to determine whether organic brain disease which tends to disorganize cerebral functions will reduce the sensory experiences to independent disconnected sensations or to simpler levels of integration of whole figures. The teaching of the gestalt school would lead one to assume that wherever there is any experience or nervous reaction some power of structuralization persists. Gelb and Goldstein reported the case of a patient who, following a cerebral injury, could not recognize the most elementary gestalten, such as a triangle, or straight or curved lines; they believed that the loss of such gestalt perception is the cause of the symptoms of agnosia, especially alexia. Holmes and Horrax reported the case of a patient, with optic agnosia associated with lesions in the bilateral angular gyri, who had difficulties in orientation in space and who could see things as wholes, but could not analyze them into parts or perceive two adjacent objects in their relationship to each other. Riddoch reported the case of a patient with a bullet wound in the right occipital lobe who could not localize objects in space and could not separate them from their background. Something of this problem has been approached in my studies of normal, defective and schizophrenic persons. These showed that the optic field is in a state of flux or movement and that optic perception arises in it from the vortical movement, which becomes progressively organized: first by perseveration of vortical, whirling or circular movement; then by accentuation of radiational movement especially in the horizontal plane, by a separation out of segments, and finally by a control of perseveration by inhibition and the gradual building up of parts derived from these elements as they tend to coincide with external stimuli. In defective adults there is a retardation at the different levels of integration of gestalten, while in schizophrenic persons there is a dissociation of the integrative function. Similarly, the spontaneous sidewalk drawings and games of children show the tendency to maturation of integrative functions established at each age level by an equilibrium between the mental symbols determined by the biologic background of the sensory motor fields and the reality of the external world. These findings lead to the conclusion that the principles of gestalt are not fixed and established by the rules of Wertheimer's gute gestalt, e.g., by proximity, continuity, similarity, inclusiveness and natural geometric figures, but depend in part on the biologic characteristics of the sensory fields at the different maturation levels and the integrative integrity of the functioning nervous system. It is the contention of the Berlin school of gestalt that the gestalten are established by organization in the sensory fields; they are not thought to be completely organized in the stimuli and simply projected on the sense organ, but the organization is something that originates as a physiologic characteristic of the nervous system. Undoubtedly organic integration is, in the last analysis, based on the same principles as those of the so-called inorganic world which furnishes the stimuli; the organism is therefore prepared to organize the data coming from the physical world in accordance with reality as though it were repeating the history of its own evolution. Köhler, it is true, conceded that "attitude" by selection and suppression in some way influences the organization in the sensory field. But one must go further than Wertheimer and Köhler and say, with Schilder and Sander, that the personal complexes, the training and the specific situation also help to determine the organization of each gestalt, and that the gestalt function or integration is not completed at the sensory level but is an active and progressive function of all parts of the nervous system, with a possible tendency, as will be shown in the course of this study, to localize in special fields in the cerebral cortex. Fundamentally, then, just as gestalt arises from a state of flux in the sensory field, so it is always in a state of flux; it is never absolutely determined and is constantly subject to modifications depending on the nature of the stimuli, the reception in the sensory organ and sensory field, the state of the nervous system in the different levels through which it passes, the totality of the personality, including the emotional complexes, and the situation or context in which the reaction occurs. In children it is clear that the integrative functions undergo processes of maturation. In the present study I am interested in following related disintegrating processes in the perceptual motor patterns as they appear in persons with organic brain disease and symptoms of sensory aphasia, and in following the reintegrating processes in the gestalten as there is evidence of recovery from the aphasia.

Sensory aphasia due to left cortical injury was first carefully analyzed by Wernicke, who, in discussing the speech functions of the area known by his name, claimed that the " 'concrete concept' of an object is a fictional or schematic conception of such an object arising as a function of radiating subcortical fibers from various sensory centers which converge into one point, a sensory speech center, and give rise to a definite group of memory images".

"Loss of memory images from a lesion in this center of the fibers radiating to it" is the classic explanation of sensory aphasia. Hughlings Jackson (cited by Head), however, claimed that the speechless person had not lost the memory for words, but was unable to produce words in propositional speech. The difficulty was thus not one of general intelligence, but of certain activities of the mind having to do with the formation of propositions.

Head defined aphasia as a functional disturbance of speech consequent on a unilateral brain lesion. He denied any significance of the distinction between motor and sensory aphasia because, since speech is an integrative function standing higher in the neural hierarchy than motion and sensation, it cannot be analyzed in terms of motion and sensation. Like Jackson, he did not believe speech to be a general intellectual capacity, but defined it as an act of "symbolic formulation and expression". Aphasia is a defect in the special mental activity of symbolic expression such that the greatest difficulty will occur in higher propositional speech or more abstract symbolization; it is not a defect in general intelligence. Agnosia is a perceptual defect on a lower functional level than that of symbolic formulation and expression. Head tended to emphasize the formulative and expressive side of speech rather than the integrative, and the symbol as a unit of expression rather than as a part of the symbolic significance of the whole. For this reason perhaps, he did not consider speech as a part of the higher integrative function, which is after all general intelligence and which would tend to rise and fall together with speech in lesions of the cerebral centers. He did, however, recognize that in aphasia the symbol is affected so far as it expresses relational processes in constructive thinking. The other problem to be considered in this connection is whether speech is a specific localizable function of certain cortical areas. Head argued against this, claiming that there is no point-to-point correspondence between the normal production of any psychic act and the independent activity of any particular group of cells. Such centers are solely integrating foci. When they are affected, certain adaptive reactions are disturbed. In other words, as the vigilance dies down, various forms of response disappear. Vigilance seems in some way to express the tone of the nervous activity which functions by way of integration and expresses itself in intelligence on the psychic side. Focal brain lesions prevent the normal fulfilment of some specific form of behavior, but nevertheless the reaction that follows any given situation still expresses the response of the organism-as-a-whole under the new conditions, or, one may say, the new-organism-as-a-whole, which is, perhaps reacting at a lower organized level or like a more primitive organism.

The recognition of speech as an integrative response of the organism as a whole was more fully emphasized by Schilder. He considered speech as a whole psychic interaction based on symbolic thinking; in aphasia the act of thinking as a whole is disturbed, owing to lesions involving different partial functions, but the nucleus of thinking or conceptional images is not destroyed. There is an obstruction in the development of progressive integration of the sensory cognition, leaving the rest of the brain to function in a more primitive way; nothing is subtracted, but more primitive responses emerge or the gestalt integration goes on at a simpler level.

CASE 1, *Plate 26*—A man, aged 65, was found to have senile arteriosclerosis with a slight hemiparesis, shown by an increase in tendon reflexes on the right and a slight homonymous hemianopia. He did not imitate movements or understand gestures; he did not withdraw from painful stimuli, and the blinking reflex was absent. He was apraxic and his power of attention was poor. He could obey simple commands, repeat simple phrases and count, but would readily become confused with more complicated material. He perseverated a great deal and was paraphasic in all spontaneous speech. Thus when asked: "What is your name?" he responded "Joe-Joe-Henry-Henry-Joe-That's my name, ain't it? Joe". "Where do you live"? "Joe-Henry-down-town-that's where I belong-I belong to Joe". He could not write his name or any meaningful letters.

On the day after admission he was given the test material to copy. The results are shown in *Plate 26*. This is an excellent example of the most simplified method of expressing the outstanding configuration principle in the test material. It is clear that he understood what was wanted, and in nearly every instance (he failed entirely in Fig. 3) he succeeded in expressing the most important gestalt principle involved in each form in a symbolic way with the least expenditure of energy. He has used the primitive round loop as his symbol for each unit in the organized whole.

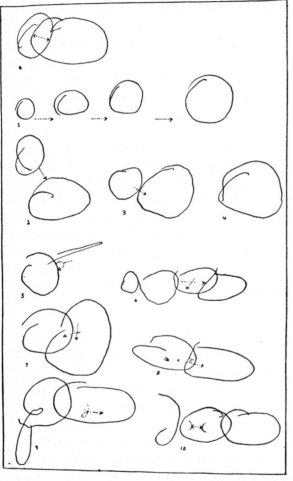

PLATE 26

In Fig. A he has two such side by side (or a little overlapping); the one to the left is a more definite circle than the one to the right—or more significantly, the one to the right is the less perfect circular loop. In Fig. 1 he has used a series of such units in the proper sequence suggested by the series of dots. Figure 2 is less complete than the rest of his efforts, but it is a relatively laborious test, and throughout his productions one sees the tendency to express relationship with the least expenditure of effort. Here he has apparently attempted to express a slanting relationship of the three unit groups. In Fig. 3 he has been satisfied to indicate that there is a form present and represents the whole as one unit. This is apparently the most difficult gestalt in the whole series; at least it proves most difficult for growing children. In any case he has shown that the form as a whole stands out against the background, and this, as Koffka has pointed out, is the first principle of gestalt integration. In Fig. 4 he has recognized and symbolized the two parts of the gestalt and their proper relationship to each other. Figure 5 is an excellent and obvious representation of the circular unit with the upper right-hand dash. In Fig. 6 the sinusoidal curve line is represented as a series of overlapping loops. The overlapping may also represent the crossing. Figure 7 again shows the two loops in proper relationship to each other. Figure 8 is remarkable because this gestalt was constructed by Wertheimer as a gestalt related to Fig. 7, with the same two units overlapping in a different way, but it is not recognized in this way by the usual normal person. That it was so recognized and represented by this patient is evident. He has flattened his loops in Fig. 8 on the horizontal plane to make clear the difference between it and Fig. 7. Figure 9 is also remarkable. The gestalt is made of two loop units, the first one slightly modified to resemble a J. By the simple use of three loops he has closely approximated Fig. 10.

Comment.—In this man, with an organic brain disease apparently due to a hemorrhage in the left temporoparietal lobe, together with the severe distrubances in the more highly integrated functions of speech, thought processes and social and personal habits, there has been a disintegration of the more intricate, internal, detailed organization in these simple sensory (visual) motor patterns. In each instance, however, the outstanding principle of the gestalt as a whole has persisted, and it has often been exaggerated. The patient's interpretation has been an adequate symbolization in which the essential configuration has been recognized. The symbol unit has been the simple, primitive, enclosed, compact loop, which represents the gestalt on its indifferent background.

CASE 2, *Plate 27*—This case is more remarkable because the rapid improvement from a state of severe aphasia following a cerebral embolism was followed with the test material from day to day. The patient, a man, a leather worker by trade, aged 43, was admitted to the medical service of Bellevue Hospital on July 12, complaining of generalized edema, dyspnea, nocturia and hemoptysis. His blood pressure was 170 systolic and 116 diastolic, and a diagnosis was made of cardiac decomposition on the basis of hypertension associated with coronary thrombosis. At that time there were no mental or neurologic disturbances. He was given digitalis and other symptomatic treatment and improved rapidly until the night of July 25, when he was reported by the nurse to be acting in a peculiar manner. On examination he was found to have a right facial paresis and to be aphasic. He was transferred to the psychiatric division on July 27. Examination there showed a slight paresis of the right side

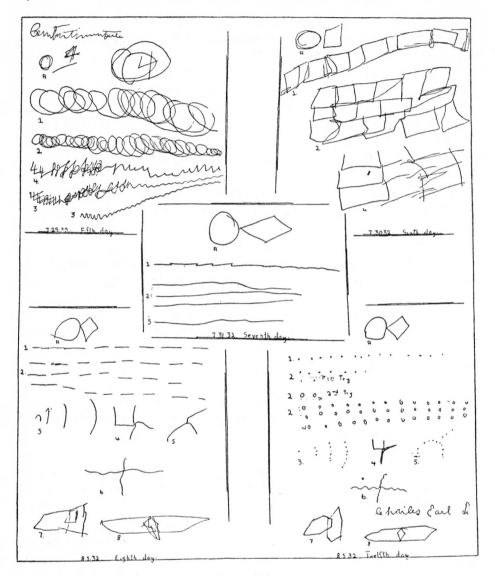

PLATE 27

of the face and the right arm; the latter was apparent from a sinking of the right arm when the two arms were outstretched, but there was no demonstrable difference in the tendon reflexes. There was no hemianopia. There was an exaggerated reaction to painful stimuli, as well as many apraxic phenomena, which were more marked in the right arm than in the left. Movements of the right arm called forth associated movements

in the left; less often the reverse occurred. There was difficulty in pointing across the body to any member of the opposite side; for instance, he
could not point to the left ear with the right hand, although he could
immediately point to the right ear with the right hand and the left ear
with the left hand. The patient tended to imitate or otherwise execute
any initial movement correctly, but thereafter he perseverated the same
movement in response to all subsequent movements or commands until
he finally became confused and blocked. On request, for instance, he
correctly imitated the movements of turning a coffee-grinding machine;
but immediately afterward, when he was asked to point to his right ear
with the right hand and the movement was shown to him by example,
he responded again with the movement of turning the grinding machine,
then became confused and gave up the effort. He was always amiable
and attempted to speak; he repeated the command, however, several
times before responding and then had difficulties in choosing his words.
He often hit on the wrong word and perseverated this until confused
and blocked. For example, when asked: "What is the matter with you?"
he responded, "Well, sir, a few days before I came I had a-a-a straw-
berry festival—well, I had a festival—like a festival—a festival—". His
effort to copy the gestalt tests showed similar phenomena. He had an apparent understanding of the problem and an initial correct response, well
organized and executed, but this response tended rapidly to perseverate
itself until its production became completely disorganized or "deteri-
orated", and his intellectual efforts were finally paralyzed. The test was
repeated daily from the fifth day after the cerebral embolism until the
twelfth day, when he made a marked improvement and was taken home
by relatives in a condition in which he was again able to care for his
own needs and carry on an intelligible conversation without mental confusion or paraphasic mistakes. He still seemed somewhat euphoric, however, and uncertain of himself.

Plate 27 shows five daily productions. On July 29, on the fifth day
after the cerebral accident, he made a good effort to reproduce Fig. A,
making a satisfactory circle and showing the proper relation between
the circle and the square, but he was less certain of the details of the
square. Dissatisfied with the results, he tried again, but did even worse
than the second time, when the circle was less well executed and the
square was placed inside of it. Actually the square took the form of a 4,
because he looked at his own first production, mistook it, and said, "Oh
it is a four". Now in attempting Fig. 1 he perseverated his own original
loop, but he interpreted the gestalt concept or sequence of units from

the test form. In attempting Fig. 2 he merely perseverated his previous response. In observing Fig. 4 (which was presented to him after Fig. 2) he may have noted a resemblance to his own 4 in Fig. A; for a while he perseverated this, but rapidly confused it with his former loop perseverations. When Fig. 3 was offered to him he again perseverated his previous response until all evidence of gestalt or organization was lost in a trailing line. When encouraged to try again he only repeated the tail end of the trailing line and then gave up the test in confusion. In the beginning of the test there appears an attempt to write his own name, which began correctly with the initial C, but ended in a meaningless scribble. This tendency to scribble, as shown both in his name and in the latter part of the test figures, may be a reversion to the stage of scribbling seen in small children and low grade defectives, a stage preceding that in which evidences of gestalt organization appear.

On the next day, Fig. A was reproduced with better confidence and execution. The only mistake, the failure to orient the square on the diagonal, is a more primitive response; it was corrected on the next day. Figure 1 on this second test was produced by a perseveration of the last part of Fig. A, the square. The idea of a horizontal sequence was represented with the square as the symbol unit. The same tendency is even more evident in Fig. 2, where he produced three horizontal sequences of squares. This tendency to interpret Fig. 2 as three horizontal lines was shown to be the more primitive reaction in the mental defectives of my previous study, and only in the higher levels were the vertical slanting groups of three loops recognized as the unit of the gestalt. The tendency for compactness, closure of open spaces, condensation of the gestalt as a whole and the resulting conservation of energy appears clearly in this case as in Case 1, but it finds a different mode of expression. Figure 4 was offered next, and it will be seen that by modifying his square unit symbol to the extent of omitting the top line of his square he produced the first part of the test figure; he then tended to perseverate his previous production with increasingly poor execution until he finally gave up the test in confusion and dissatisfaction. Definite progress, however, was made on this second day; interestingly enough, the progress was in the organization of the gestalt as a whole rather than in the details. The patient eventually failed because of his uninhibited tendency to perseverate the same details until he was unable to adapt them to the test pattern. Then he became dissatisfied, confused and blocked.

On the seventh day he executed Fig. A correctly. He then attempted Fig. 1 as a new problem and showed that he was aware of the problem.

Each little indentation in the horizontal line was a representation of the sequence of the dots. In the motor pattern this was more evident because he stopped momentarily at each indentation. At the end of the line the indentations are less evident, but they were also marked by pauses as he performed the test. Figure 2 was performed in the same way as the three parallel forms of Fig. 1. With Fig. 3 he started in the same way, became completely confused and gave up the test.

On the eighth day, Fig. A was correctly formed. Figure 1 was this time broken into interrupted lines; before, he had merely interrupted his movements in the construction of a continuous line. Figure 2 was again drawn as three parallel forms of Fig. 1. Figure 3 was now attempted, and the main principles of the gestalt were represented by horizontal lines. Figure 4 was fairly well done. Figure 5, like Fig. 3, was represented by continuous lines. Figure 6 shows the essential organization of the gestalt. Figures 7 and 8, however, were both looked on as composed of three figures in horizontal series, as a result, possibly, of his previous experience with horizontal series in Figs. A, 1, 2, 3 and 4. This day's record shows great improvement, mainly through his increasing ability to inhibit the perseverating influence of the immediately preceding response.

Between the eighth and twelfth days little new was accomplished. But on the twelfth day he reached that point in the learning (or relearning) curve, emphasized by Yerkes and Köhler in apes as well as in man, which is due to sudden insight into the problem as a whole. Figure A, as usual, was well done. Figure 1 was shown properly as a sequence of dots. In approaching Fig. 2 he showed his usual tendency merely to repeat the structure of Fig. 1; then he suddenly said, "Oh no—it is round holes". Thereon he started his usual horizontal sequence of "round holes"; he again stopped and said, "Oh no—it is three round holes". He at once produced his gestalt in a normal way. He hesitated a minute with Fig. 3 saying, "It is dots". Then he rapidly produced this in the correct way and continued with the rest of the test with confidence. At the end of the test he laid down his pencil with a sigh of relief saying, "Well, now it is all right, isn't it? Can I go home?" At this time he was also able to write his name correctly (to avoid identification the end of the name is not reproduced).

Comment.—It is of no small interest to follow the course in this case of aphasia; in motor behavior, verbal speech and visual motor patterns (copying of gestalt) the patient showed the same tendency to understand the problem and approach it in a well organized attempt, which was, however, soon frustrated by an uninhibited tendency to perseverate the units of his own response. The role of gestalt in the organism-as-a-whole was clear. The outstanding features in the responses were: (1) The larger principles in the organization of the gestalt were more significant and persistent than the details, and were often exaggerated; (2) there was a tendency to revert to more primitive reactions such as are seen in children and mental defectives; (3) there was a tendency for more compact, enclosed, energy-saving responses than the stimuli suggest; (4) there was a tendency to use unit symbols influenced by the preceding principles and to represent relationships within the gestalt as a whole by these; (5) there was a marked tendency to uninhibited perseveration (a) of the unit symbol, (b) of the preceding responses or (c) of the principles of the organization, and this tendency was likely to lead to confusion and finally complete blocking or paralysis; (6) recovery from the cerebral insult showed the same type of progressive integrative maturation, with episodes of sudden insight into the problem as a whole which is shown in normal developing and learning in human beings and anthropoids; (7) in this recovery or relearning, the larger principles of the relationships of the gestalt appeared before the details of quality of form and distances of space, or in Wertheimer's terms, of proximity and similarity.

CASE 3, *Plate 28*—This patient showed some rather severe apraxic symptoms as well as some motor disability in the right hand owing to a mild right hemiparesis. His productions are interesting, however, especially because of his tendency to perseverate his own mistakes and finally arrive at a paralyzing confusion as in Case 2. His errors usually arose from misinterpreting a series of dots as writing of some sort. In the other gestalten, in which the organization was on a broader principle, he showed a remarkable capacity to grasp and reproduce the gestalt principles in spite of his rather severe aphasia and motor disability.

The patient, a man, aged 60, was a dishwasher who suddenly collapsed over the dishwashing machine and was unable to talk. At the hospital we found him to be senile with the usual deteriorative and arteriosclerotic changes. The retinal vessels were sclerosed. Further, he had a right facial weakness, weakness of the right arm, causing clumsiness and tremulousness of all movements, and a distressing numbness. He was insensitive to pain, especially in the right arm. He was amiable and cooperative, but apathetic and bewildered. Although he was awkward and slow, he was able to care for his personal needs. His speech was unintelligible, but he understood a few simple commands and imitated a

few simple movements. He could not scratch a match; he dropped it
and did not know that he had done so.

When offered the test material on the eighth day after the cerebral
accident, he had difficulty in handling the pencil and was awkward and
slow. Still he produced Fig. A fairly well, although the square was not
diagonally oriented, and the circle was produced only by a number of
small segments. When Fig. 1 was offered him, however, he repeated the
last part of his previous performance, the square. On seeing that this
was wrong, he drew lines through it; getting the idea of a capital A

8 days after cerebral accident.   10 days after cerebral accident.

PLATE 28

from this and the concept of a sequence from the test Fig. 1, he started
the A. B. C's. After he produced the first three letters, an effort was
made to divert him and start him again on the copying, but he persisted
in writing the alphabet. This time he continued until he became confused.
When offered Fig. 2, he repeated the same performance on both the
first and second trials. Each time he lost the sequence as well as the
ability to form the letters accurately just at the letter E. This block was
not due to fatigue, for he was able at once to start again and to execute
the first part of the series better on each succeeding trial.

Two days later, when he seemed more alert and somewhat improved,
he was offered the test again. Figure A was produced about as be fore,
although with somewhat better motor facility. Figure 1 called forth an
attempt at sequential writing; it was an almost unintelligible scribble,

although the initial letters each appeared to be the letter W, the first letter of his name. Figure 2 and the figures made up of a sequence of dots, namely, Figs. 3 and 5, called forth the same response. But the other figures (4, 6, 7 and 8) were well organized gestalten; the lines, however, were broken and irregular because of the motor disability. These productions show that the larger principles of organized gestalten may be retained while the finer principles involving the sequence of dots and small circles call forth other forms of organized sequence; the other forms were here, in one instance the alphabet, suggested by a self-performed error, and, in another instance, a primitive scribble which was perhaps an effort to write his own name.

CASE 4, *Plate 29*—A man, aged 59, had aphasia and left hemiplegia on the basis of cerebral arteriosclerosis. The patient always had been left-handed. He had a left external strabismus. Aphasia tests showed that spontaneous speech was paraphasic and perseverative. He obeyed simple commands poorly; he could not repeat series of numbers or names, nor could he read or write to dictation. He had a finger agnosia. His percep-

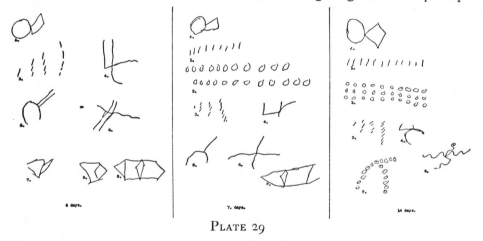

PLATE 29

tion of pain was poor. He tended to be euphoric, but readily broke into tears. He showed no apraxic symptoms. He was restless at night and needed supervision in his personal care. He talked constantly, and realized that something was the matter with his speech, but always pointed to his teeth, which were in poor condition, as the cause of his difficulty. When asked to draw the picture of a man, he did so very poorly, and then said: "That is supposed to be a lady. I can't suppose very good, but that is what it is—supposed to be a lady. That makes the ladies children—for instance, a lady like you—that makes the children. Still I would work you know—and show where it is and say it is all right. It is my teeth. After I used to be able to work and could work, but after my teeth got this way—it got this way. I could show you right from the start". His conversation always went in the same way. However he started, he would make some incoherent remarks about children, then try to explain his present disability, explain that his teeth interfered with his speech, insist that he could work and ask that he be given a chance to do so.

The same perseverative tendencies were seen in his gestalt productions (*Plate 29*). When the tests were given five days after admission, parallel oblique lines tended to perseverate in Figs. A, 4, 5, 6 and 7. Figures A and 5 were remarkably alike, and so were Figs. 4 and 6. The first attempt to make Fig. 8 resulted in a gestalt similar to the preceding Fig. 7. The patient showed a rapid improvement in clinical symptoms, and two days after these tests was able already to inhibit the tendency to perseverate and showed an ability to individualize each figure instead of producing the second figure as a variation of the preceding one.

A week later, his productions were probably about normal for his intellectual level. A right-sided cortical lesion in this case was productive of a disturbance in the gestalten with aphasia because the individual was left-handed.

CASE 5, *Plate 30*—This case is of interest because of some knowledge of the localization and extent of the lesion which produced a sensory aphasia with relatively little disturbance in the perceptual-motor gestalt function as shown by the copying of these test forms.

The patient, a man, aged 27, had had one year of college education. While under the influence of alcohol at a party he fell over the banister to the floor below, alighting on his head. He was brought to the hospital in a stuporous condition which persisted for several days. Roentgen examination showed multiple fractures of the vault of the skull on both sides. There was a bilateral Babinski reaction, and on the fourth day there developed right-sided convulsions with paralysis of the right side of the body, including the face. A diagnosis of laceration and hemorrhage in the left motor region was made, and five days after the accident he underwent a decompression operation in the left frontal parietal region, which revealed laceration and maceration of the underlying brain, subdural multiple hematoma and intraparenchymal hemorrhages. Dural vessels were tied; part of the dura was cut out, and free blood, blood clots and macerated brain tissue were removed. The remaining brain looked blue and contained many hemorrhagic areas. The patient improved immediately, however, and in a few days there was no right hemiparesis, recurrence of convulsions or other neurologic deviations. As he began to speak, he showed a severe sensory aphasia with the following features: He was restless, especially at night, and noisy, but always

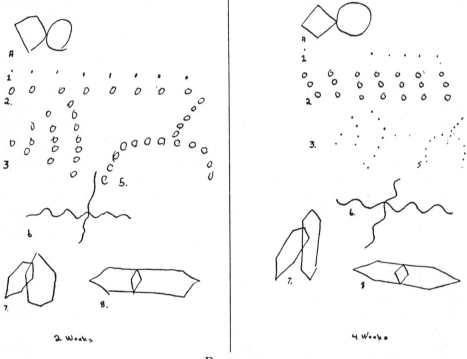

PLATE 30

euphoric, with some manic behavior. He talked continually in a facetious strain with many paraphasic mistakes. He was unable to name objects and showed a finger agnosia. He had difficulty in understanding any commands or questions, whether spoken or written. He also made paraphasic mistakes in writing. When asked to count to ten he said: "one-two-three-any G — d — thing. All right, who can't count to ten? I would do it—any one could. Two—it must be very—. Same G—d—thing. Where did you get that nice one (referring to the stenographer)?" He wrote a letter to his mother: "Dear mother—I am wanting meeting. I am myself leaving meetings. I am feeling fine". Although still somewhat euphoric and paraphasic in talking and writing, he went home much improved at the end of a month.

His productions in copying the figures are seen in *Plate 30*, two weeks after the accident when he still showed a severe aphasic disturbance, and one month after the accident when he was much improved. The remarkable thing about this case is that the disturbance in gestalt integration was so slight in view of the gross cortical lesion in the left frontal parietal region and the rather marked sensory aphasia. Considering the extent of the lesion, however, it is also of interest that there was such a marked improvement from the aphasic disturbance.

Even two weeks after the accident, when the aphasia was still severe, the gestalt productions might be considered nearly normal if it were not for the fact that the patient was of high intelligence and had had a year of college work, which included some mechanical drawing. The productions two weeks later were entirely normal from any standard, and in comparison with these the earlier productions show features of a lower level of intellectual integration. The work as a whole was done with less precision; Fig. 2 was produced by a single horizontal row, and Figs. 3 and 5 with loops instead of dots, while the angulation in Fig. 3 was not well shown. All of these features, however, were corrected in the later productions.

Summary and Comment

In studying the gestalt function in visual motor patterns by means of copied form in eight cases of organic brain disease in which sensory aphasia was a conspicuous symptom, the following observations were made:

Case 1 showed a disintegration of the more intricate, internal, detailed organization of the gestalten, with a perseveration of the fundamental, outstanding gestalt principle by the use of the primitive loop as the unit symbol. Nothing of the building stones of perception but only the intricacies of the higher integrative capacities were lost by the cerebral lesion; the organism-as-a-whole continued to respond at a more primitive level by establishing a new equilibrium between the test forms and the mental symbols of the more primitively functioning nervous system.

Case 2, which we followed day by day through the course of recovery from sensory aphasia, showed the following tendencies in visual motor responses: (1) perseveration of the larger principles of gestalt; (2) emergence of primitive responses; (3) utilization of the compact, enclosed, energy-saving unit symbols to show relationships; (4) perseverative tendencies that led to confusion and blocking; (5) recovery accompanied by progressive integrative maturation with sudden episodes of insight. This case shows that the external object, in this case the test forms, is not the only factor in perception, but that the external and the internal situations play a large role. The external situation includes other objects in the field, both in time and space. In these experiments, the preceding test forms frequently modified the response to subsequent forms. This is as important a factor as space in optic perception; as Katz has shown, and as I have also shown, movement is the first element in preception. Kanner and Schilder have shown that movement is always present in optic imagery.

Perseveration arises more from temporal than from spatial factors and may in some way be compared to the aftereffects in sensibility experiments. Thus one gestalt is modified by the previous one if the aftereffects or temporal perseverations have not yet subsided or been inhibited.

CASE 3 showed complicating symptoms of apraxia and motor disturbances. Nevertheless, the fundamentally principles in the gestalten are expressed, however laboriously.

CASE 4 showed tendencies to perseverate from one figure to the next with a loss of individualization of form when the fundamental principles were still perserved. This occurred with a right cerebral lesion in a left-handed man.

CASE 5, that of a man of high intelligence, showed a slight tendency to a lower level of integration of perceptual motor gestalten following a lesion of the left frontal parietal region with a sensory aphasia.

It is generally supposed that in sensory aphasia the first third of the gyrus temporalis primus of the dominant hemisphere is affected. The question arises as to whether such a lesion also produces the disturbances in the visual motor gestalt function which are described in this paper, or in other words, whether one deals with the same psychologic mechanisms in the gestalt functions as in other symptoms in these cases with sensory aphasia. It is at least possible that the gestalt disturbance is due to a lesion of parts adjacent to Wernicke's area. The disturbance in the gestalt function does not run absolutely parallel to the degree of sensory aphasia. Case 5, with a severe sensory aphasia, showed only a minimal disturbance of the gestalt functions. In this case the lesion seemed to extend from the temporal lobe more in the frontal direction, while in case 1, with a maximal disturbance, there was a slight homonymous right hemianopia, indicating an extension of the lesion toward the occipital pole. In the other cases, the neurologic evidence was not sufficient to determine which parts besides the Wernicke area were affected. In every case but one the symptoms pointed to a lesion in the left hemisphere; the one exception was a right-sided lesion in a left-handed man. One may conclude therefore, in a general way, that the lesion which produces this disturbance in the gestalt function either coincides with the Wernicke location or lies nearer to the occipital pole in the temporoparietal region. Gelb and Goldstein have reported the case of a patient with a lesion in the occipital region who showed a complete word-blindness and a complete loss of power to recognize the most elementary gestalten, while sensory aphasia in the common sense was absent. In the cases reported here, primitive functions of gestalt not only were perserved, but were even exaggerated. It seems that the gestalt function is more involved the nearer the lesion comes to the occipital region. It is probable that the gestalt function is not strictly identical with the sensory speech mechanism, but merely allied to it. Thus, in a general way, we may conclude that the area most probably involved in disturbances of the visual motor gestalt function, as exemplified by these copied test forms, is that between the temporal, parietal and occipital lobes of the dominant hemisphere.

Orton has emphasized the different levels of visual function, the simple perceptive level being about the calcarine fissure, while the visual recognitive and associative level surrounds it. The visual motor gestalt function would seem to belong to one of the higher levels, probably the associative.

Speech and gestalt functions are integrative functions of the personality-as-a-whole, with the cerebral cortex as their highest center of integration. Speech is based on symbols arising from the interplay of the stimuli of the external world and the sensory field in any given situation or context. The properties of the sensory field are determined by the laws of its biologic nature which are limited by the maturation level, the integrative integrity (lack of lesion), the status of the personality, including the emotional complexes, and the given situation. Lesions in the higher integrative centers would change the response to a lower integrative level, with the emergence of primitive tendencies which may modify each other in such a way that the response varies from case to case and day to day depending on the total result of all the factors involved. These factors include the basic biologic matrix, the previous maturation level, the integrative level permitted by the specific lesion, the locus of the lesion and the emotional complex of the individual-as-a-whole.

These studies of disturbances in perceptual motor gestalten in organic brain disease indicate that the gestalt principles are never fixed, but are the integrative response of the personality-as-a-whole in any given situation; in disintegrating cerebral lesions they tend to revert to more primitive levels, and, as the brain recovers from its insult, they tend to follow the laws of developmental maturation in returning to the higher integrative responses.

CHAPTER VIII

THE DISTURBANCES IN VISUAL MOTOR GESTALTEN IN DIFFERENT TYPES OF ORGANIC BRAIN DISEASE*

DEMENTIA PARALYTIA

A RECENT INTENSIVE review of the various features in dementia in general has been made by Scheid; this should be referred to for the literature. Kraepelin's analysis of the symptomatology of dementia paralytica is in some way still classic. He emphasized that in the domain of intellect one of the first changes is often a difficulty in perceiving and understanding outward impressions—"The patient is absent-minded, inattentive and does not grasp events transpiring about him with accustomed clearness". Kraepelin discussed the inability to fix the attention for a long period at a time, with more or less clouding of consciousness, disturbances in retention and memory and disturbances in orientation and time relations. His analysis of the paralytic disturbances in handwriting is well known. Schilder has made a most intensive study in the psychology of dementia paralytica. Instead of the old concept of a defect he offered a new concept of a changed attitude and an insufficient technic in thinking. The process of thinking comes to a premature conclusion because attention is defective and unsuitable methods of thinking are used. Normally, the processes of thought include perception, the working over of the material and recollection. Schilder's experimental material was the repetition of a short story that was told to the patient. He was dealing with auditory perceptions, concepts and configurations, which are organized in time instead of the visual patterns of my material which are organized primarily in space. He emphasized that one is concerned with wholes and parts and their relationships. In the process of hearing the story the normal tendency is to anticipate the whole story with each sentence and thus organize it as a whole from the beginning. If this anticipatory adjustment fails, there remains only a word to word conception without regard for the sense of the whole. This anticipatory adjustment appears to me in some way to be a temporal gestalt function. Schilder showed that as the story proceeds the adaptation requires that some anticipations be accepted and others rejected. In the patient with dementia paralytica there is a lack of interest in the whole relationship associated

*From the Arch. of Neur. & Psych., 1935, 33; 1-24.

with the lack of anticipation. In perception the patient receives only whole impressions and does not adapt them to the newly added material and to his own life experiences, to his general effectivity and specific complexes as the normally integrated person does. Normally the working over of the material is merely a fuller understanding of the perception with further analysis and correction against experience, affectivity and the whole situation. The same occurs in recollection; there are always new combinations, selections and corrections. The patient with dementia paralytica does not correct sufficiently in this way, his critical power is diminished. He does not check against logic and experience. His general affectivity is weakened. His consciousness of the thing being right or wrong is weakened. Furthermore, an error once made is persistently followed. Perseveration occurs as a primitive feature. This is closely connected with a once accomplished configuration. The impulse to continue and conclude may be diminished but at the same time there may be an increased impulse to productivity of a rhythmic motif by perseveration. Another feature is that the patient does not place the episode properly in its setting. The story is not considered as a historical event but as an experience of his own. The bringing together of individual parts into a whole does not occur, and if a total concept comes to completion it is not sufficiently structuralized. The outstanding characteristic of the content of the production of a patient with dementia paralytica is its banality or commonplaceness. While in the schizophrenic patient the disturbance occurs in the complex determined material, in the patient with dementia paralytica it occurs somewhat more in the periphery of the psychic life, although not so far in the periphery as in aphasia and apraxia. In the patient with dementia paralytica the disturbance takes place in the superficial layers of fairly well developed concepts; the utilization of the concept is changed; there is a failure in the working over of the material, in the combining, correcting and checking of it, and there is a weakness in the consciousness of what is correct. There is a disturbance in the differentiation and integration of the parts of the psychic experience.

In discussing the question of gestalt, Schilder took issue with the Köhler Koffka, Wertheimer school, which clamed that the gestalten are determined at the perceptive level. Schilder claimed that there is a constant remodeling, a production momentum—not only a gestalt but a gestaltung. He maintained further that the gestalten at all levels are influenced by attitudes and experiences and by the general affectivity and the specific complex. He claimed that it is the active remodeling or combinations in gestalten that are affected in dementia paralytica, while in aphasia and agnosia both the passive reception of the configurations (gestalten) and the reconstruction (gestaltung) are effected.

A general summing of Schilder's analysis may be expressed in these terms: The patient with dementia paralytica is not interested in the structure of things, in the nature of the parts, in their relation to the whole or in the relation of the whole to the context; furthermore, he shows a defective power in any active structuralization tending to lead to productions resulting from the adaptation of his receptive experiences to the world of reality. The developing child has certain impulses in the motor sphere and certain vortical characteristics of the perceptive fields. His problem is to produce symbols from these two functions which represent the external world. The demented person has lost the urge to make these adaptations, the

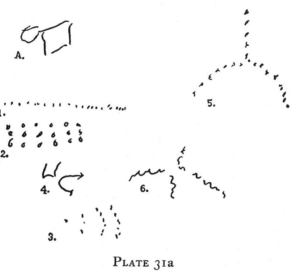

PLATE 31a

power to perform the processes of correcting and selecting and the consciousness of his own error. He has also, as a resurgence symptom, the primitive motor impulse to perseveration of his own poorly consummated configuration.

CASE I, *Plate 31a*—A colored woman, aged 30, was transferred to the psychiatric division of Bellevue Hospital on August 6, 1931, from the City Hospital; a diagnosis of dementia paralytica was made. She had been at the City Hospital since December in a semicomatose condition; the Wassermann reaction of the blood was 4 plus, and the serologic condition of the spinal fluid was typical of dementia paralytica; routine antisyphilitic treatment had been administered. On admission she said: "I was all dead about Christmas. It was nice there, but I just got sick and tired of it. It seems now and then my mind goes away. I was dead three times, you know. I forget the name of the hospital".

The pupils were fixed to light; speech was defective to test phrases and was slurred. The patient was childish, emotionally unstable and confused. Memory was defective and she was entirely disoriented. Speech was incoherent, disconnected and fragmented.

Gestalt Forms.—The patient's productions in *Plate 31a* shows tendencies to make the figures very small and to fragment and separate parts. The tendency to draw figures very small or to write small—micrographia—has been described by Gerstmann and Schilder, who claimed that it occurs as a result of a weakening or poverty of the impulses. It is found associated with various diseases of the brain, such as encephalitis and sensory aphasia, and in the latter may occur only in the hand innervated by the hemisphere which contains the lesion. This patient not only produced small figures, but sketchy ones. Separation of parts of the figure tends to emphasize the primary members of the gestalt, as in Figs. 2 and 4. Fragmentation, however, further divides the figure, usually in places not recognized by the gestalt principles; thus squares, which are genetically simple closed figures, are fragmented into sides, and the crossed wavy lines are fragmented into four wavy lines and further fragmented into segments of the waves.

In this case, then, a patient with dementia paralytica, with prolonged comatose periods, and episodes of confusion with no real interest in the situation, showed in visual motor gestalt responses a poverty of impulses, a tendency to fragment the structure of the gestalten at points not always in keeping with genetic principles, but determined by the superficial appearance.

In an intellectual person incipient dementia paralytica shows rather typical features in the production of these visual motor gestalten, which may be characterized by a certain stilted, excessively careful perfection that tends to be formalistic and to lack any personal interest, while at the same time there are nearly always some evidences of reversions to some primitive tendencies.

CASE 2. *Plate 31b*—A man, who appeared to be about 40 but who could not recollect his correct age, claiming he was 24 or 26 years old, had had one year of college education and had been an actor. He was brought to the hospital as a prisoner on a charge of disorderly conduct because of resisting an officer who attempted to make him "move on" from a box on the street where he had been sitting for a day and a night.

The Wassermann reactions of the blood and spinal fluid were four plus; there were 20 cells in the spinal fluid, and the colloidal gold curve was

0122332100. He said that he had had antisyphilitic treatment for one year. There were incomplete Argyll Robertson pupils and slurring speech. The patient was dull and lethargic and would lie on the bed all day; he took no interest in anything except that he showed occasional outbursts of irritation. He could not calculate or recall accurately. He said: "I was sleeping on a fire escape—a landing. I had a box to lay on. The fellow took it. I asked them for it, and he would not give it to me so I kicked it from under him and I picked up a brick".

The patient carried a drinking glass wrapped in paper. About this he said: "I don't want to drink after people. Why, I might get a disease. I took the cure for eight months. I must have gotten the syphilis off a glass". He was told that he seemed sluggish. This made him irritable. He said: "So that makes me insufficient? It does not. I don't have to take this off of you people. I will get out of here tonight".

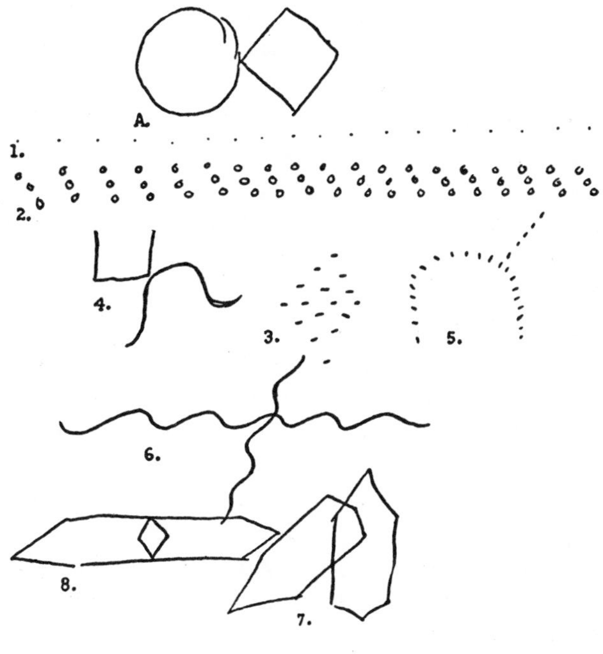

Gestalt Forms.—The patient's productions on *Plate 31b* show excellent qualities. Note especially the correctness in Figs. 7 and 8.

PLATE 31b

The stilted formalistic features are exaggerated in Figs. 4 and 5, and as a result the configuration in Fig. 4 is destroyed; the difficulty, however, is not in making angulated forms, which is the problem in normal genesis, nor in the tendency to exaggerate a series of arc forms, which is another common difficulty. The use of some substituted form, such as, in this case, the dash for the dot, is a characteristic feature of dementia paralytica, which will be discussed in subsequent cases. Primitive tendencies are seen in the monotonous perseveration of Figs. 1 and 2 to the edge of the paper.

Comment.—Several cases of dementia paralytica in which treatment with malaria or with the radiothermy technic had been used in the New York Psychiatric Institute have been studied by this method. The majority have shown the features of the group just described, namely, a formalistic, impersonal perfection with one or another feature suggesting either some form of reversion to primitive responses or some feature more or less typical of dementia paralytica. It should be said that most of the patients treated had possibly been selected for treatment because they were in the early stages of the disease and were originally of adequate intelligence; consequently they show the features of this group. It should also be said that they were all patients who had returned to the hospital because they had in some way failed to adjust in spite of the treatment.

In cases of productive dementia paralytica one finds a number of new features. One such case had already been discussed briefly from the point of view of differential diagnosis from mental defectiveness. One of the most conspicuous features was the substitution of various letters or numbers for the dots in the dotted figures. Thus, Fig. 1, instead of being a series of dots, was the series of the alphabet from A to K. Figure 2 was then made as three horizontal series of M's and N's and finally McC's, the patient's own initials. Figure 5 was made of 8's; Fig. 4 was made like a single large 4, while the patient said: "That is not a four, I guess". In addition to Fig. 4, others were also constructed with wrong configurational principles, for example, Fig. 5, and Fig. 8 was made with the ends expanded instead of pointed. I may summarize by saying: The structure of the gestalten is partially ignored (1) by disorienting them from their background, (2) by constructing them by principles suggested by their superficial appearance rather than their genesis and (3) by substituting some other figure for individual parts. The patient's own initial may be used, or some other familiar but inappropriate series may be substituted for the one offered.

Similar features are shown in the following cases:

CASE 3, *Plate 32*—An Englishman, an oiler, aged 64, who had been in the United States for twenty years, was brought to the hospital in November 1930 as a prisoner on a charge of vagrancy. He had small irregular pupils, which did not react to light. The knee jerks were diminished. The Wassermann reactions of the blood and spinal fluid were 4 plus; the colloidal gold curve was 5544321000. The patient was confused and amiable and presented Korsakoff features. Comprehension and memory were poor. He said: "Yes, of course I know where I am, but I don't know if you do or not. I'm right here. You ought to know that".

Gestalt Forms.—The productions (*Plate 32*) show an excellent perfection of the general configuration. Dots, however, are always converted into figures. Figure 5 is disoriented on its background; Fig. 6 is fragmented at the point of crossing.

CASE 4, *Plate 33*—A white man, aged 30, had been treated with malaria in a private hospital the year before, but the disease had continued to progress. At home he was threatening and hit the baby, so that the wife was afraid of him. He was dull, incontinent and unable to care for his personal needs. Speech was totally disorganized, irrelevant, incoherent, paraphasic and dysarthric. He said: "I am all right. He gave me gas. I sleep with gas. Give me temps in the ear. Good doctor—Bellevue Hospital—I mean what a doctor give the good weight 135. My boy is —I mean my wife— but the boy—I mean my wife hit the boy— I mean my son—I love my son (cries)".

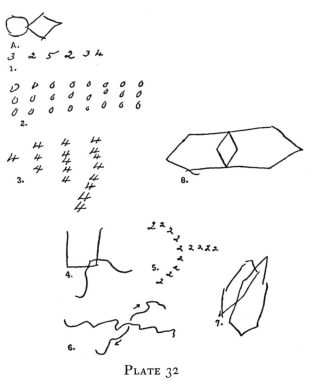

PLATE 32

Gestalt Forms.—The productions (*Plate 33*) showed the primitive use of combinations of loops in Figs. A, 4, 6, 7 and 8, and in Figs. 1, 3 and 5, the use of dashes and numbers, characteristic of dementia paralytica. In Fig. 3 the patient has accurately represented the configuration in terms of numbers, counting each horizontal series of dots and offering the number in place of the form. Figure 5 may represent some similar effort. At the top is the patient's attempt to write his own name, John J —.

Summary.—When patients with dementia paralytica are asked to copy test figures various types of visual motor gestalt responses are produced, depending in part on the type of clinical syndrome. It would be of interest to correlate these responses with the localization of the lesions in the brain. The level of the original intellectual integration is probably also sgnificant, as well as the personality as a whole and the situation. The higher intellectual levels are seen in the general contours and attempts at perfection in the productions. From time to time the patient's initial or other personal material is worked into the gestalten. In the dull

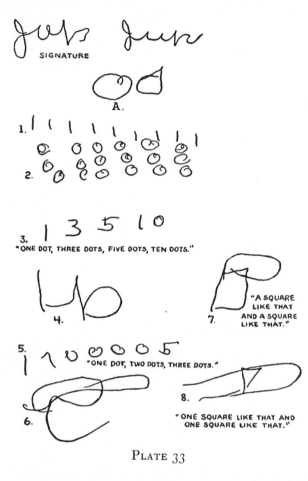

lethargic types, prone to comatose episodes, the visual motor gestalten show evidence of poverty of impulses and of fragmentation at artificial points in the configuration suggested by the superficial appearance rather than by the genetic gestalt principles. It is possible that cases showing these features are those in which the lesion is more basal than cortical; this is suggested by the associated lethargic states and is compatible with the published reports of cases of epidemic encephalitis showing the same feature. In the expansive types there is a tendency to substitute letters, numbers, dashes or the patient's own initial for parts of the configuration, while

PLATE 33

the whole figure remains fairly intact. This may be akin to confabulation. The whole figure may be disoriented on its background. Later, it will be shown that this is a confusional feature. Parts of the form may be changed; thus, the two ends of Fig. 8 may be expanded, but nevertheless the whole figure remains nearly intact. The general principles of the gestalt are preserved at all times. Some change of a minor nature happens to the concept after it is correctly conceived as a whole. One has the feeling that it is somewhat playful but rather senseless. Occasionally a form is copied in a way contrary to the gestalt principle, while the patient remonstrates with himself and says, "It is not really that". Early cases of dementia paralytica in well integrated persons or cases in which treatment has been administered early show certain compensatory features. There is a tendency to formalistic but impersonal perfection. Nearly always, however, there is also some telltale feature suggesting one or another type of paralytic deviation, or reversion to some primitive feature such as the use of the closed loop or perseverations in horizontal dextrad directions. These primitive reversions are more common in cases with aphasic, agnostic or apraxic features.

ALCOHOLIC PSYCHOSES

There are a variety of mental disturbances caused by acute and chronic alcoholism, such as encephalopathia alcoholica with its typical organic lesions in the brain, which often progress to death, the Korsakoff syndrome, often associated with peripheral neuritis, acute and chronic delirium, acute and chronic hallucinatory states and acute confusional states, and various mixtures of these syndromes. In a psychologic, clinical and pathologic study of alcoholism Schilder and I have differentiated the encephalopathic group from other types and have analyzed the symptomatology in relationship to the organic lesions in the brain. Clouding of consciousness is in the foreground of the psychologic syndrome, in which difficulties in perception play the most important part, associated with some delirious and confusional features, with difficulties in the integration of the perceived pictures. The picture is perceived incompletely and is not well integrated into the whole, or the whole is not well differentiated into its parts. With the clouding of consciousness are associated motor difficulties which are characteristic of this disturbance. They are rhythmic movements, especially of the arms and hands, associated with grasping, groping and pointing. Because of other features, such as poor attention and lack of cooperation, tremors and tensions in the arms and ocular disturbances, patients with encephalopathia alcoholica do not lend themselves well to this test.

CASE 5, *Plate 34*—In this atypical case of encephalopathia alcoholica, the patient died a few days after having attempted to draw Fig. A of the test group. There are three efforts to draw the figure, each starting with the square and never attempting the circle, but becoming diverted each time by some perseverative behavior. The first time the patient continued the incompleted sides of the square into perseverated tails; the second time he made many perseverated strokes over the incompleted figure; the third time he completed the square but continued the last side into a dextrad stroke across the paper and then started to enclose the square in loops which are perseverated down the paper in simple strokes. In this case one sees the combined effect of the perceptive and motor disturbances typical of this disease. The picture is never completed as a perceptive pattern, and finally the visual motor pattern is distorted by the motor impulse to rhythmic movement.

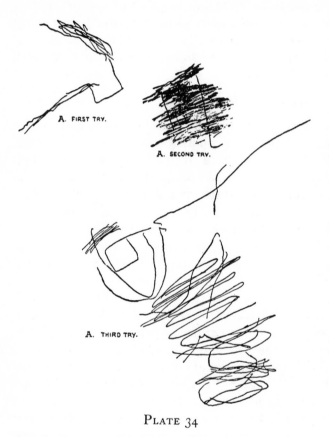

A. FIRST TRY.

A. SECOND TRY.

A. THIRD TRY.

PLATE 34

Comment.—The Korsakoff psychosis is differentiated from the encephalopathic state by the clearing of consciousness. The difficulties in the integration of the material is held to be more pronounced than the perceptive difficulties, and there are active tendencies to confabulation because of these integrative difficulties, especially of past material or memories. Bonhoeffer, in an analysis of the mental symptoms of the various types of alcoholic disturbances, recognized the perceptive difficulties and showed that they do not arise in the periphery or perceptive organ but are of central origin. On account of these disturbances and the slowing down of the mental processes there arise difficulties in the construction of an accurate picture of the outside world. That there are difficulties in the reception as well as in the working over and reproduction of material will be seen in case 7, which, however, in the beginning also showed some confusional and organic features.

CASE 6, *Plate 35*—A woman, aged 50, a college graduate and a school teacher, was admited to the psychiatric division of Bellevue Hospital on June 9, 1932, with a clinical picture of alcoholic encephalopathy. She was emaciated and unable to walk, and lay helpless in bed; she was incontinent, tremulous, drowsy, confused and disoriented, with defective memory and confabulation. The pupillary responses to light were defective; speech was slurring; there was a general tremor; the tendon reflexes of the legs were hyperactive; the muscle bellies and nerve trunks were tender. There was a history of chronic alcoholism. The Wassermann reaction of

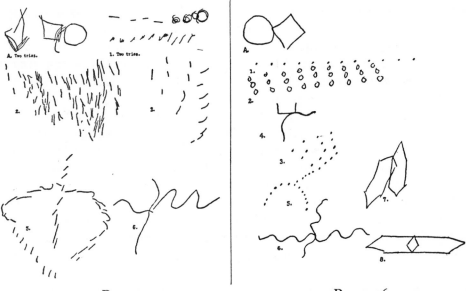

PLATE 35   PLATE 36

the blood and spinal fluid was negative; the colloidal gold curve was 0011000000. On admission the patient could not cooperate with the test, but two weeks later, on June 21, she was improved and no longer toxic or tremulous; although she was still weak and the limbs were tender, the condition appeared more like a Korsakoff psychosis with peripheral neuritis. She was amiable, euphoric and talkative, confabulated and showed defective memory. The pupillary reaction to light was present. She was cooperative with the test, anxious to do well; she made a great effort but was dissatisfied with the results.

Gestalt Forms.—The productions (*Plate 35*) which were scattered over six sheets of paper, are reproduced only in part. The results are in many ways similar to those in Case 5 (*Plate 34*) a case of progressive encephalopathy. They show the same difficulty with individual parts of the whole figure and the same tendency to interrupt an incomplete figure by strokelike perseverations. These are not perseverations in form, but are perseverated motor impulses such as were described in the rhythmic movements in the encephalopathic cases. They are often brought into play by making passive movements of the arms of the patients, which they will then continue rhythmically. This patient was herself baffled by her difficulties and attempted each figure many times, but invariably became distracted by some rhythmic process. From the results, however it is clear that she was working with some concept, even though an incomplete one, of the test form in mind. In Fig. 2, for example, she started the figure with three distinct downward dashes, which are to be seen on the left side of the figure; she continued the motor pattern and soon distorted the figure and had difficulties in stopping. The continuation of the last stroke in Fig. 3 and of each extremity, especially the central dash of Fig. 5, is also seen.

Two weeks later the patient was much improved. She was able to walk and to care for her personal needs. She was clear and oriented. At this time she produced the test figures in an entirely normal manner (*Plate 36*) and without any uncertainties. A couple of weeks later she was discharged from the hospital as recovered.

Comment.—A Korsakoff psychosis with less organic features and more confabulatory and confusional features is seen in the example given in my differential diagnosis from mental defect. There are some tendencies to revert to primitive responses, to disorientation of the figure on its background and to changing dots into X's and 2's; these phenomena were seen in patients with an expansive type of dementia paralytica and appear to be a confabulatory feature.

CASE 7, *Plate 37*—A Scotchman, aged 49, was admitted to the hospital on July 11, 1932, in a state of alcoholic excitement—tremulous, agitated and disturbed—which passed into a hallucinosis. He did not recover in two weeks; on July 27 it was neccssary to transfer him to a state hospital. The Wassermann reaction of the blood was negative. Apart from the tremulousness there was no organic feature. The patient had vivid auditory and visual hallucinations of a distressing nature. He said: "Yes, I see my wife laid out there in her coffin. They shot her last night. I heard all about it over the radio. I was the one that put the spark in the air. They are going to kill me in front of her tonight. But we love each other too much". A week later, on July 18, he was no longer acutely toxic, but still had hallucinations and was subject to emotional episodes of fear and remorse.

Gestalt Forms.—The majority of the gestalten are well perceived as a whole (*Plate 37*). The patient has surrounded Fig. 4 with an outline to emphasize the whole contour and multiplied the internal figure in Fig. 8, as he said, "For good measure." The outstanding feature is the technic in forming the outline for the figures. There are some evidences of motor tremulousness and a tendency to go over and over each outline, which is undoubtedly similar to the tendency observed in the other alcholic psychoses with more profound organic involvement. It is possible that the outlines are also hazily perceived; nevertheless, the gestalt as a whole is well perceived and reproduced. Three days later the figures (*Plate 38*) showed considerable improvement; as gestalten they are well done, but there is the same tendency to repetitious movements in the outlines. There are no confusional features.

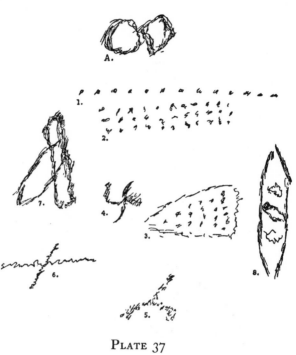

PLATE 37

Comment.—The alcoholic confusional states can perhaps be considered with the other acute confusional states. However, for the sake of comparison with other alcoholic conditions one example will be given here.

Summary.—Gestalt disturbances in alcoholic psychoses are best approached with an understanding of the severe alcoholic encephalopathies, in which the progressive lesions about the ventricles of the brain may lead to death. This organic disturbance is associated with deep clouding of consciousness, with perceptive difficulties resulting in incompletely perceived gestalten and motor difficulties with increased impulses to rhythmic movements. By this combination the visual motor gestalten in copied figures are profoundly disturbed, so that the figure is reproduced incompletely and is distorted by perseverated strokes. In less severe conditions there appear the Korsakoff psychosis, with less clouding

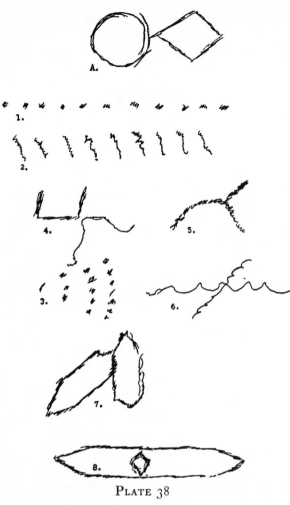

PLATE 38

of consciousness and more features of disturbed motor impulses in the perservative tendencies of the figure produced. This is a perseveration of motor impulses or rhythmic movement and not a perseveration of form such as is seen in the sensory aphasias, although even in the latter the perseveration probably has a large motor element. In chronic alcoholic hallucinatory states the gestalt as a whole is well perceived, but the outlines are hazy, perhaps partly from perceptive difficulties, partly from tremulousness and partly from the motor impulse to reiterate the line. In the confusional states there are less marked motor difficulties, but the perceptive difficulties are in the foreground and show disturbances in the integration of the parts into the whole and in the orientation of the figure on its background.

TRAUMATIC PSYCHOSES

Recently, Schilder has analyzed the psychic disturbances after head injuries in patients in the psychiatric division of the Bellevue Hospital, many of whom were tested with the gestalt test. Schilder discusses the analysis briefly and publishes illustrations. His analysis shows that following the initial state of loss of consciousness there is a stage of deep clouding of consciousness with disorientation in time and space, bewilderment, helplessness and retardation in perceptive functions, leading to difficulties in synthesis of the primitive impression into integrated wholes. "The gestalt function is deeply impaired. In the visual motor gestalt patterns, primitive structures appear. . . . It is probable that the clouding of the consciousness, the perceptive difficulties and the disturbances in the gestalt function are partially independent from each other, but they are closely interrelated with each other and influence each other". He shows that the chronic Korsakoff picture may follow the acute posttraumatic confusional picture, which is distinguished from it by the absence of clouding of consciousness, and that in this posttraumatic Korsakoff state there may or may not be disturbances in perception and gestalt function. The patient whose posttraumatic Korsakoff psychosis he describes in detail showed only minor disturbances in the gestalt function in the way of more primitive responses. However, there are posttraumatic Korsakoff states which show rather severe disturbances in motor gestalt responses. The difference in the reaction is possibly· due in part to the localization of the lesion in the brain. In the more acute stages the whole brain is in some way involved. There is a general congestion and edema, with bleeding in the subarachnoid space, and in cases which I have observed, universal perivascular hemorrhages, especially about the ventricular system, such as are found also in encephalopathia alcoholica. Russell claimed that all parts of the brain suffer and that the site of the injury is of little significance in most cases. Bennett and Hunt emphasized the multiple punctuate intercerebral hemorrhages, cerebral edema and subarachnoid hemorrhages, which tend to lead to a diffuse cortical atrophy. Such pathologic changes appear to be associated with deep clouding of consciousness and disturbances in the synthesis of perceptive and gestalt functions. More specifically localizable lesions may of course lead to more specific defects. Case 8 in my report on sensory aphasia presented these features; there was a fracture of the skull, with gross injury to the left frontoparietal region, and a primitive type of reaction in the gestalt function typical of sensory aphasia; the productions improved rapidly as the sensory aphasia improved after operative treatment.

CASE 8, *Plate 39*—A man, aged 42, who was admitted to the psychiatric division of Bellevue Hospital on December 13, 1931, after having been injured in an automobile accident on December 5, had been found lying unconscious on the sidewalk. He had sustained an irregular fracture of the right side of the base of the skull and a depressed fracture of the left parietal bone. There was a left hemiparesis; the pupils were dilated and irresponsive, and there was nystagmus. The patient fell to the left when in the Romberg position. He was emotionally dull, but amiable, and there were Korsakoff features. Speech was slurred, but he was not aphasic. He said: "This is New Year's Eve. The accident was a month ago on Christmas Day".

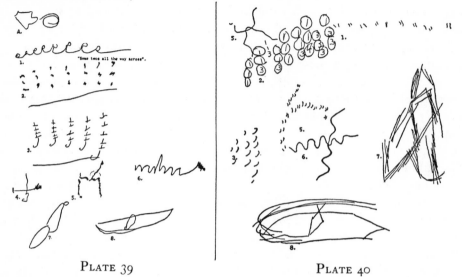

PLATE 39   PLATE 40

Gestalt Forms.—The patient copied the gestalt test on December 31 (*Plate 39*) and produced some rather bizarre forms. In general the gestalt principles are intact, though in a somewhat primitive form. There is serious distortion of the internal configuration of Figs. 4 and 6. There is no spatial disorientation typical of confusion. However, the individual parts of the configuration are distorted. Figure 1 is "some 2's all the way across", so that the figure becomes a dextrad horizontal series of connected 2's instead of dots. Figure 2 is a dextrad series of triads of jagged dots instead of loops. Similarly, Fig. 3 is a dextrad series of progressive lengths of crosses with a loop at the bottom. The other feature is the tendency to put loops or broad tails on nearly every figure. This shows some of the same features as the expansive type of dementia paralytica and the confabulatory type of alcoholic Korsakoff psychosis, with possibly some motor impulses to extra loops and tails.

CASE 9, *Plate 40*—The patient was transferred from another city hospital to the psychiatric division of Bellevue Hospital on December 24, 1930, after having been hit on the head and knocked down while drinking, eight weeks previously. He was dull, confused and bewildered. He was not clear as to his environment and wandered about in a confused way. He confabulated constantly. Memory was defective for recent events, and he could not tell anything about the accident. He was retarded mentally and physically. He walked on a wide base and tended to veer to the right. There were flattening of the right side of the face, ptosis of the right eye, weakness in the right arm and slurring speech. Roentgen examination of the skull and examination of the spinal fluid gave negative results. He said: "I know where I am, but I forget the name of the hospital. I was down at the Post Graduate this morning (not true). I had an examination of my head. There is nothing the matter that I know of. The doctor came in and had a patient and asked me to give him a hand to bring him in. I brought him, and then he asked me to bring him to the Polyclinic Hospital. I did, and then he turned on the doctor. I interfered, and in the meantime I got hit in the mouth. A big crowd came into the clinic and into my home. I didn't know them; they were just noisy bodies".

Gestalt Forms.—The visual motor gestalt productions (*Plate 40*) show certain characteristics of the Korsakoff features such as were shown in cases of expansive dementia paralytica and alcoholic Korsakoff psychosis. The general gestalt principles are intact, though the individual parts of the figure are modified or replaced, but not in such a way as to interfere with the configuration as a whole. Dots are duplicated in Figs. 3 and 5; the loops in Fig. 2 are filled in with numbers. The outlines in Figs. 7 and 8 are reiterated several times. Both motor and sensory impulses appear to play a part.

Summary.—The acute confusional stage following head trauma is characterized by clouding of consciousness with difficulties in the synthesis of the perception and gestalt function. Visual motor gestalten produced by the copying of figures show reversion to primitive features and confusional features, which are seen especially in the disorientation of the whole figure on its background. As the clouding of consciousness clears, and a chronic Korsakoff picture is left, there may or may not be disturbances in perception and gestalt function. In some cases in which the injury is apparently severe and associated with signs of neurologic disturbances, Korsakoff features appear in the visual motor pattern. They are characterized by retention of the configuration as a whole and proper orientation of the figure on the background, but with a tendency toward some reversion to primitive responses and with modifications or substitutions in parts of the figure in such a way as not to interfere with with the structure of the gestalt. These features seem to be related to the confabulatory tendencies in speech and to pathologic motor impulses.

ACUTE CONFUSIONAL STATES

Acute confusional states occur in all forms of intoxication, whether endogenous or exogenous. They may also occur in connection with organic diseases of the brain and sometimes with schizoprehnic or manic-depressive psychoses. Schilder described the confusional states (or amentia) with perplexity as the central manifestation, in which "perplex-

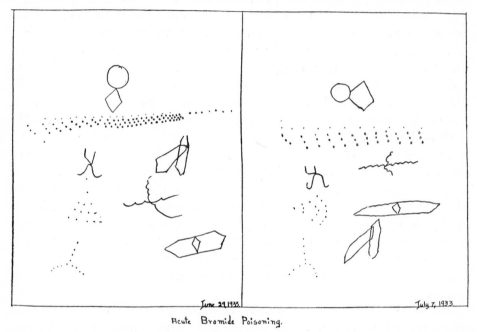

Acute Bromide Poisoning.

PLATE 41

ity is the correlate of an inadequate comprehension of the environment with the additional symptom of dissatisfaction with the inadequacy".

Confusional features have already been shown in dementia paralytica (*Plate 32*), in alcoholic confusional states (*Plate 37*) and in post-traumatic confusional states, with the following features: (1) some moderate degree of reversion to more primitive responses, (2) some difficulties in integrating parts of the figure into the whole gestalt, (3) a nearly specific tendency of disorienting the whole figure on its background. The last feature has appeared to be the most characteristic of the confusional state. The figure itself is complete but is upside down, in mirror reversion or turned around at an angle of 45 degrees. In the gestalt theory, Koffka has claimed that the first principle is the relationship of the figure to its background. The background may be looked upon as a part of the gestalt and this disturbance in orientation as a disturbance in the most fundamental principle in gestalten. In other terms, the background is the environment, and this disturbance may be considered as an adequate comprehension of the relation of the visual motor pattern to its environment. In still other terms, it may be considered as a disturbance in spatial

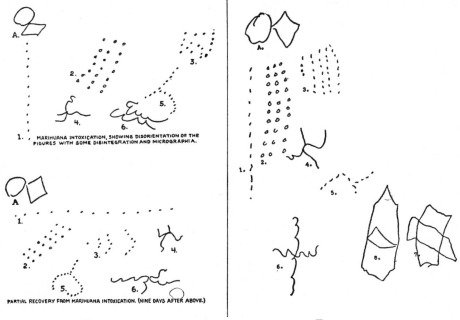

PLATE 42   PLATE 43

orientation. This feature may also be seen in schizophrenia. It may be demonstrated in any type of confusional disorder in organic or toxic states. I have observed it also in postoperative conditions, chorea minor, cardiac conditions, bromide and marihuana intoxications and postepileptic confusional states. The following cases are selected examples of the last three conditions.

CASE 10, *Plate 41*—A woman, aged 36, came to the hospital following the ingestion of an excessive amount of sodium, potassium and ammonium bromide in a fit of despondency over a runaway husband. She was lethargic, but somewhat agitated and emotionally unstable, and was constantly struggling against the urge to sleep. She was somewhat tremulous, and the tongue was coated. She appeared toxic. She seemed bewildered and complained of feeling "mixed up in her head". Speech was slurring and tended to become incoherent as she talked of her troubles. She was clear as to the episode that led to her admission.

Gestalt Forms.—The patient performed the visual motor Gestalt test on the day of admission (upper part of *Plate 41.*) There is apparently some tendency to micrographia, which is in keeping with the drowsy state. Several figures are disoriented on their background, especially Figs. A and 3. There are primitive features in Figs. 1 and 2, in the tendency to make Fig. 1 a simple dextrad series, to make Fig. 2 a mass and to perseverate in both unnecessarily. Figure 3 also shows the primitive feature of arcs instead of angles. There are some difficulties in the integration of Fig. 4. A week later, the productions (lower part of *Plate 41*) were much improved.

CASE 11, *Plate 42*—This case of marihuana intoxication has already been reported at length by Bromberg among a series of cases, in several of which the visual motor gestalt test had been performed. According to Bromberg, this condition shows among other symptoms "in the visual sphere a primitive level of perceptive integration". Case 8 in Bromberg's series is characterized by him "as an admixture of toxic features due to marihuana with psychotic features of a functional type . . . a schizophrenia on symptomatic basis". The patient, a negress, aged 31, had been smoking "reefers" and was admitted to the hospital because of peculiar behavior. She was dull, inattentive, apathetic, surly, suspicious and bewildered. She described the typical motile, colored visual hallucinations as well as hallucinations in other fields.

Gestalt Forms.—Two days after admission the patient copied the gestalt figures as they are seen in the upper part of *Plate 42.* Nearly all the figures are disoriented on their background; there is some tendency to micrographia, with some difficulties in the internal integration, as in the crossing in Fig. 6, and a consequent reversion to more primitive tendencies. Nine days later (lower part of *Plate 42*) the visual motor responses were much improved, although minor difficulties still persisted in Fig. 2.

CASE 12, *Plate 43*—A negress, aged 42, was suffering from a post-epileptoid confusional state in which she was dull, disoriented for time and place, bewildered and unable to get about the ward to care for her personal needs. She was also very irritable.

Gestalt Forms.—The productions (*Plate 43*) show the same features of moderate micrographia, which are to be associated with the dullness, as are seen in connection with the lethargic types of dementia paralytica:

disorientation of the figures on their background, as in Figs. 1, 2 and 6; difficulties in the integration of Figs. 3, 4 and 7 and secondary primitive reversions.

Summary.—The disturbance in acute confusional states resolves itself into a disturbance in the integration of the parts of the figure to the whole and of the whole to its background or situation. The primitive reversions are secondary to this primary difficulty. When micrographia occurs it is associated with the poverty of impulses observed in cases showing lethargy or dullness.

CHAPTER IX

SCHIZOPHRENIA

My FIRST STUDIES* with visual motor gestalten were with schizophrenic patients at the Springfield State Hospital of Maryland. There I found schizophrenic patients who had shown catatonic characteristics for years but who had in the beginning of their illness been studied at the Phipps Clinic of Johns Hopkins Hospital. The following three cases are examples.

ALMA B. (*See Plate 44*) was an orphan. She reached the eighth grade and then became a nursemaid in a family, where she cared for six growing

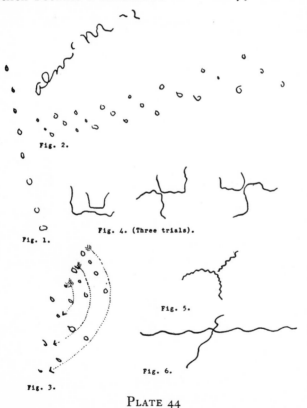

Fig. 2.

Fig. 1.

Fig. 4. (Three trials).

Fig. 5.

Fig. 6.

Fig. 3.

PLATE 44

children until she was 35, when she was no longer needed and was relegated to the attic to sew. She became depressed and seclusive, and had the idea that men on the street were watching her. She went into a religious ecstasy, and said she had the power of healing and the power of conception. In the Phipps Institute she explained that she had been lonely and wanting love until she found it in Jesus, and after that everything was changed and she was happy. At the Springfield State Hospital she said that she was the second Virgin. That was fifteen years ago. After that she had had two remissions during which she got along fairly well in the outside world, until she went into a catatonic

* From the Arch. of Neur. & Psych., 1932, 27; 661-686.

stupor in which she was mute, soiling, tube-fed, resistive and irritable. In the course of several years she passed from this into a hebephrenic state, associated with a marked tic of the lips, in which she ejected saliva in an explosive tonic click whenever she initiated speech. She identified other patients as the children that were formerly her charges. Her speech showed marked dissociated schizoid features, and there was an incoordination of the muscles of the face, hands and of the gait.

In her productions there are many interesting features. Her inability to write her own name, owing to fragmentation and perseveration of parts, is shown. In general, her productions show the characteristics of a mental level of from 7 to 8 years. Dots are interpretated as loops, and yet the function of slanting appears. Many disorientations appear. Figure 1 was produced in a vertical plane though the figure lying before her was in the horizontal plane, so that at the completion of the task the two forms lay before her at right angles to each other. As will be seen later, this occurred frequently. In Fig. 2, the slanting of the first vertical plane initiated a slanting of the whole figure. This was seen also in the nonschizophrenic persons of lower mental levels and probably is in line with the tendency to counter clock-wise movement which is accentuated by the slanting form. Figure 3 requires careful analysis, but the principles involved are simple and the same as have been seen before. Dots are given as the primitive loop. Beginning at the left there is first the single loop and then in proper relation to it three more with a suggestion of angulation. In the next plane, the upper three are properly placed, but the lower two are separated from the upper by a considerable distance, and in the last plane, though the upper four are properly placed, the lower three are again separated to the same degree as in the previous series. Thus, the left and upper part of the figure is correct, but the right lower part is dissociated by the clock-wise movement; but the separation is not in accordance with the gestalt principles. What determines the parts disturbed is not apparent. The patient made three efforts at Fig. 4 and finally succeeded in the third effort. The second is wrong only in that the lower bell-shaped figure is approximated to the lower left corner of the upper figure rather than to the lower right corner, but in the first effort, besides this the lower figure is also turned upside down. Here the individual parts are determined in accordance with the principles of gestalt, and the difficulty in associating them is a disturbance of a higher integrating function. It seems characteristic of the schizophrenic subjects that one part of the figure is disoriented in relation to another part, or that the dissociation of parts is so marked that one part does not help in the orientation of another. To see the patients actually struggle with these simple forms is very impressive. They are obviously painfully disturbed by their difficulty in accomplishing what seems such a simple task. Even at the end they often seem in doubt as to whether they have finished the task satisfactorily.

EDNA S. (*See Plate 45*) came of a fámily in which many on both sides were psychotic and mentally defective. Three others besides the patient had been in the Springfield State Hospital. After the death of the father, she and the mother went to live with a widowed maternal cousin when she was 14. She never helped with the housework, never had any friends or associates, and never held a position for more than a few weeks at a time. At 29, she began to talk about being engaged to her widowed cousin and implied that there had been illicit relations. This was all denied by the cousin. She said that she was being talked about, suddenly became excited and said that she had become color-blind, that every one was rushing about and crowding around her and acted as though they had bad news to tell her. At the Phipps Institute she was confused, suspicious

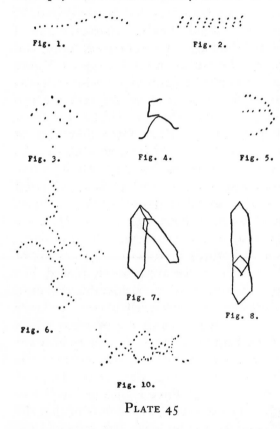

Fig. 1.

Fig. 2.

Fig. 3.

Fig. 4.

Fig. 5.

Fig. 7.

Fig. 8.

Fig. 6.

Fig. 10.

PLATE 45

and resistive. She felt that someone had put a spell on her and spoke of being persecuted by Catholics, Germans and her family, and she talked of religion and war. Examination after ten years showed that she was apathetic, soiling, needing constant nursing care, manneristic, blocked and fragmentary in speech, and using numerous neologisms. There were tremors and incoordinations of the fine muscles of the hands and face, and the pupils were inactive to light.

Her reproductions, *Plate 45*, show some interesting points not brought out in any of the previous ones. There is a marked tendency to micropsia, seen especially in Figs. 1 and 2. There is a tendency to perseverate from one test form to the other, especially in regard to the use of dots, as seen in Figs. 2, 6 and 10, There is a tendency to change the horizontal plane to the vertical, as has been seen before, in Figs. 3, 6 and 8. Owing to rotation, which is a more primitive tendency than horizontal planes, there is a tendency to dissociate parts of a figure by disorientation, seen in Fig. 4 and especially in Fig. 5, where the half circle is rotated in the clock-wise direction, and the upright stroke is actually placed inside. Here again one sees that, though the tendency to rotate this figure is apparently accentuated by the position of the upright stroke, still this member itself is dissociated from the figure, and the rotational movement of the whole figure is very strong; thus the dissociation is obviously functional and not complete. It may be said, therefore, that the rotational form is characteristic of schizophrenic dissociation, and that it is never an immutable tendency and never total or regular in its functioning.

The rest of the patients were persons whose original intellectual endowment was average or higher. It might be assumed that the higher the intellectual level, the greater the number of possible dissociations as the integrative and associative functions are more elaborate.

MAE L.'s (*See Plate 46*), father of whom she was very fond, committed suicide when she was fifteen. She had "nervous prostration" after this for several weeks. She quit high school in the second year and took up stenography. But in her work she was overconscientious and sensitive, and became increasingly worried about her inadequacy and tendency to preoccupations. She felt that her fellow employees were talking about her. She quit two positions at twenty-one because she felt inadequate. She became sleepless and self-reproachful and spoke of her family being disgraced and killed by her masturbation. She became blocked in speech, saying German spies were listening to her. At the Phipps Institute she became stuporous, nearly mute and incontinent; she was tube-fed and resistive, demanding release because "I ought not to be here". For six years (to the time of writing) her behavior has been the same, except for an increasing apathy and diminishing interest. Her only spontaneous productions were, "Too late" and "Father" and "I ought not to be here".

In copying the test forms (*Plate 46*) she showed some obvious difficulties. She tried them over several times and seemed definitely puzzled.

Thus in her four efforts at Fig. 3, which are not altogether intelligible, the principles of gestalt seem to be in the foreground. In Fig. 4 there is a dissociation by spatial separation and a slight disorientation of the lower part. Her three efforts at Fig. 5 show in the first a tendency to carry over from the former figure both as to size and form, and in the use of a continuous line inclosed at the bottom (horizontal plane) instead of the upright stroke being applied. The third effort is satisfactory, though there is still some effort to close the figure at the bottom. Figure 6 is of interest. In her first effort she accomplished two lines lying end to end, one having a little upright stroke. Thus there is a dissociation by directional distance and rotation, and also the horizontal plane is accentuated and the lines are not crossed. In the second effort she brought the lines closer together, tending to make them parallel and accentuating the upright stroke. The third effort carried this a little further, but she never got them together or got them crossed. In Fig. 7 there is also a wide separa-

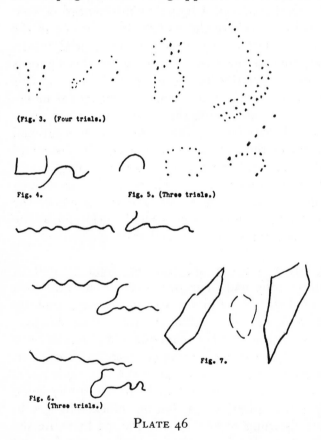

(Fig. 3. (Four trials.)

Fig. 4.

Fig. 5. (Three trials.)

Fig. 7.

Fig. 6.
(Three trials.)

PLATE 46

tion of the two parts with some apparent confusion about the space between them. One almost seems justified in assuming that the little formless figure between them is some effort to account for a space that she is in doubt about.

The dissociation that occurs in schizophrenia in the visual motor patterns as they are illustrated by these patients shows the ever-present tendency for sensory motor patterns to revert to the more primitive principles and to express movement in some way. But in the case of schizophrenia the reversion is not a simple one back to any one recognized level of development. The general principles of the gestalt patterns express the original intellectual level of the individual. There are, however, evidences of dissociations even in individual figures with partial reversions to some single principle. It may be expressed, as it is here demonstrated, as a change in rate or direction of movement in a part or whole of the pattern. Thus there may be a disorientation or spatial separation of a part of the figure by a movement in the radial direction on the horizontal plane, or by a rotary or vortical movement to an angle of 45°. This may take place in some integral part of the picture, thus tending to exaggerate the principles of the gestalt entirely or disregarding such a principle; or it may involve the whole of the figure. There are tendencies to revert to other more primitive principles by perseveration; carrying over from one figure to the next; changing dots to loops; fragmentation, representing dotted lines as wavy lines; micropsia; and accentuation of the horizontal plane, avoiding crossed and angulated forms; as well as failures to integrate the whole configuration, or to properly relate some one or more parts to the whole. It may be said by way of summary of these observations that, in these catatonic schizophrenics we note the principles of reversions back to primitive principles and dissociation, or splitting of the visual motor patterns in a way that is contrary to the inherent principles. These two features are recognized as typical of all the reactions of the schizophrenic.

In the case of a more active schizophrenic individual a more bizarre reaction was obtained.

ROSIE S. (*See Plate 47*) was a Russian Jewess. She developed her first symptoms of mental illness at the age of sixteen when she thought she was being followed, and rapidly developed a catatonic stupor. After that she had spent most of her time in various hospitals although her parents had twice removed her in order to arrange a marriage and in the hope of being cured she had also given birth to a child. Her behavior had fluctuated from long periods of stupor to shorter periods of activity during which she was playful, erotic, reacting to erotic hallucinations, talking of fanciful marriages, denudative, destructive. At the time she was examined she was thirty-four years of age. She was fairly active; giggling, touching various objects, muttering to herself, talking a great deal but in such a way that she would not be understood and she perseverated words or repeated what was said to her. She continually made grimaces and was stiff and cataleptic. When asked to draw the figures she never completed a single figure. Her first response was appropriate but she wandered immediately from the stimulus and destroyed the gestalt completely by many inappropriate lines. Her response was flighty and never returned to the goal. Unlike the manic individual with flighty responses, however, the original stimulus was entirely lost and the configuration destroyed although all of her responses had much in common and seemed to be following some pattern of ner own, and were partially, at least, dependent upon endogenous problems, one of which was her own name. This is seen in her response to Figs. A and 8 which are reproduced in *Plate 47*. In response to Fig. 2 she scattered some dots over the sheet of paper and, rapidly connecting them with lines, called her finished product a picture of "Relationship". She labeled the picture "Relatoistionshipp".

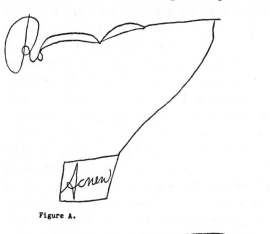

Figure A.

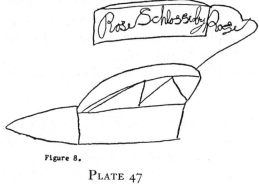

Figure 8.

PLATE 47

In this individual whose catatonic state is characterized by considerable activity, we see the tendency for bizarre and dissociated responses in which she destroys the configuration, modifying it in accordance with her own inner impulses. Freud has pointed out that in schizophrenia there is a libido impoverishment of the outside world leading to delusions of world destruction. Schilder states that the feeling of world destruction may be so marked that the patient no longer concerns himself with sense impressions of his environment; or the environment is viewed as a semblance or deception. We must assume that where the world is perceived in such a way that it will also be reproduced in such a way when the opportunity arises. Thus in this woman who was tested at a time of some activity, she accepts the challenge of the test but never continues with the stimulus at its face value. Furthermore, there is no sharp distinction between external stimuli and internal complexes. Every sensory pattern represents her struggle to determine her own identity. Simple visual patterns become for her difficult problems in abstractions and "relationships." Storch has shown how schizophrenic thought utilizes perceptual experiences and symbolic images as interchangeable, thereby giving to the thinking certain magic qualities which are well represented by this woman's playful handling of visual motor gestalt in order to solve the problems of her identity and the philosopny of "relationship".

FRANCINE (*See Plate 48*). Schizophrenic children show similar tendencies. Schizophrenia in children is rare, so rare that usually psychiatrists do not agree in the diagnosis. Francine, however, was a ten year old child of probably superior intellectual potentialities who came under our observation on the Children's Ward at Bellevue, with a symptomatology which led every physician who saw her to agree that she was afflicted with schizophrenia. In her motility she showed catatonic features with constrained postures and bizarre activities such as twirling her saliva out of her mouth and onto her dress with quick automatic movements. She showed an imbalance of the vegetative functions with cold extremities, mottled skin episodes of cyanosis and faint-like episodes during which she seemed quite sick without evident cause. Her social behavior was inappropriate; her association with other children was impersonal; her

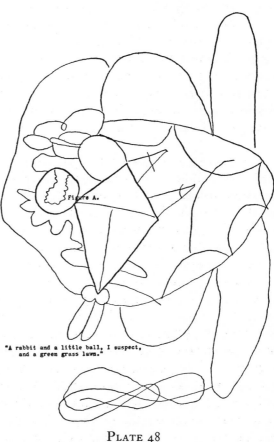

"A rabbit and a little ball, I suspect, and a green grass lawn."

PLATE 48

emotional reactions were inadequate and lacked spontaneity. Her thought processes were dissociated; she could not attend to her lessons, she experimented with words and concepts in a way that gave a philosophical turn to all of her utterances. She was preoccupied with dilusional ideas especially in regard to body structure and function, sexual problems and her relationship to her mother. Her art production was of special interest. It was evident that she experimented with space and other abstract concepts, (form.) Later, she made remarkable caricatured photographic portraitures of people in a mechanical way. She drew Fig. A *Plate 48*) correctly to begin with, but immediately began experimenting with it—both destroying the gestalt of the model and experimenting with new forms that were only slightly connected with the original, and in no way conforming with the original stimulus. Like many children she gave it a name, but, her name for the picture conformed with her customary speech mannerisms: "I suspect", and involved a rather complex concept, "A rabbit and a little ball, I suspect, and a green grass lawn". One can see the motive of the rabbit's ears appearing again and again in the drawing but in a distorted way. Of course the rabbit did not belong to the original figure although the ball does, and the green grass lawn may be the background which is fundamental to every gestalt.

In the visual motor gestalt function in schizophrenia, therefore, we find the fundamental disturbance of splitting expressing itself by a dissociation in the gestalt figures which often distorts them fundamentally so that the gestalt principles are split. This can be understood, if we realize that all form arises from motion, which is vortical, and that the schizophrenic disturbance in function is such a fundamental one that there tends to be disturbance in this motion which distorts the form of the units and the relationship of the gestalt configuration. This occurs especially in the more or less completely preoccupied catatonic. In the more active catatonic individual there is a tendency either to experiment with the form and relate it to more abstract concepts, or to fail to separate it from the abstract problems of the personality. It is seen then that the integration of the gestalt involves many fields of experience including the central problems of the personality. We find, therefore, that in schizophrenia there is not only an abnormal dissociating and splitting of functions that should remain as wholes, but that there is also a failure to dissociate functions which tend to stick too closely together so that the experiences of the personality may be represented by any unwieldly conglomeration.

CHAPTER X

MANIC DEPRESSIVE PSYCHOSES

IN THE MANIC depressive psychoses the organization of the personality is more intact than in schizophrenia, the disturbance in psychic functions being less profound. There is a disturbance in affect and in psychomotor activity; there is a preoccupation with personal problems of love, aggression and power; there is a diminution or increase in mental association. Rorschach spoke of "association energy" and referred to a loss of such energy in depressions for which reason depressed persons showed a poverty of responses to the Rorschach tests, with stereotyping of the association processes and a reduction of movement and color responses (Quoted by David M. Levy and S. J. Beck). The Rorschach test consists of a number of standard ink blots, and the person examined is expected to name what he sees in these blots, or of what they remind him. Levy and Beck also used this test on manic depressive individuals and found that they obtained results which indicated an increased "energy of association" with sustained flight attention, while in depressions, they noted a sharp perception of obvious forms, and a loss of play in association processes together with a loss of kinesthetic and color responses.

The psychoanalysis of depressions has emphasized the compulsive phenomena associated with sadistic-anal (and homosexual) level of instinct regression (Freud). Schilder has also said that in the milder depressions there is no disturbance in organized thought construction, although the thought stream may be inhibited or slowed up. It is Schilder's contention that this inhibition is an expression of the individual's aggression against himself and which will not allow him free play of his emotions and associations. The manic, on the other hand, is continually overcoming his unpleasant past memories and conflicts; this releases the energies and gives a great sense of power. There are some depressions associated with perplexity, guilt, uncertainty and doubt, of which Hoch and Kirby speak of a sensory unreality complex; there is doubt concerning the reality of the perceived experiences. Schilder has shown the relation of such cases with mental confusion and demonstrated that they have difficulty with perception; that they have difficulty in putting the details of the picture in relation to the whole; and that the doubt is based upon the imperfection in perception. There is also a disturbance in the time concept which disturbs the organization of thought processes and the perception of integrated pictures. Severe distortions result from changes in the motility of the background of perception. The severity of these disturbances depend upon the depths of regression of the instinctive life. This is due to the strong sadistic trends and aggression which one turned against the person himself and also the extent to which the personality is disorganized.

When manic depressive individuals are given the gestalt test, there are many who are too depressed and inhibited to respond to the test at all.

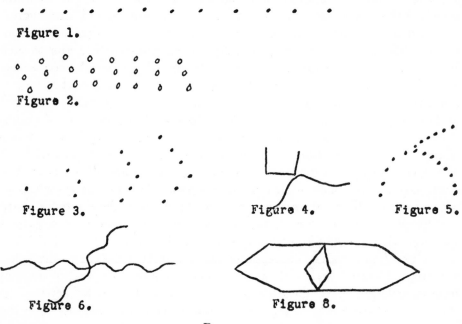

Figure 1.

Figure 2.

Figure 3.　　　　Figure 4.　　　　Figure 5.

Figure 6.　　　　Figure 8.

PLATE 49

There are also many manics who are too irritable to comply or too excited to attend to the test. The milder depressions usually reproduce the configuration with an accuracy and nicety that seem to eliminate all personal elements and suggest a compulsive carefulness; erasures and careful efforts at correctness are not uncommon; neither do they express satisfaction with the results. The milder manics will produce the same type of reproductions, but in shorter time and with some expression of satisfaction.

E. W. B. (*See Plate 49*) was 31 years of age when she was observed in her sixth episode of depression. Five of these had been associated with childbirth. Her mother, two maternal aunts and two sisters had received hospital care for manic depressive episodes. In some of her psychotic episodes E. W. B. had shown some features of excitement, bewilderment and of distrust. At the time she was observed, she was retarded and inhibited. She was mainly preoccupied with family problems, blaming herself for failing to care for her children. She showed, however, an ambivalent attitude towards her husband, dreading to return to the possibility of another pregnancy, but feeling that he did not take a sufficient interest in her. She applied herself to the drawings in *Plate 49* with great interest and drew each one with meticulous care—as the results will show.

E. van N. (*See Plate 50*). The bewildered depressions will produce configurations with many features akin to the Korsakoff or confusional states

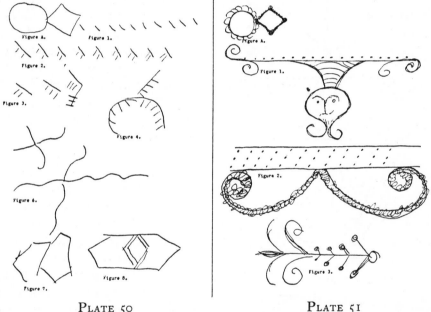

PLATE 50   PLATE 51

but with distortions which are superficial and do not tend to destroy the essential gestalt principles. *Plate 50* was produced by E. van N., a woman of 58 years. Since the birth of her daughter eighteen years before, she had suffered from recurring episodes of depression of five months' duration every year. She was usually retarded and inhibited with some short periods of excitement. On this occasion she showed marked bewilderment with anxiety. She complained that she could not express her thoughts and could not talk or even use her mouth in eating. It may be noted that in every figure the fundamental gestalt principles are well expressed, although the deviations indicate some uncertainty or doubt in the details. It also appears that the patient has used the shadow image or the negative of the real figure as in Figs. 2, 3 and 5, where one feels that the long lines are used to indicate the essential directions, and the short dashes the relationship between the dots or loops. It is as though she would not give herself or us the satisfaction of experiencing the details correctly but only in a negative form.

G. B. (*See Plate 51*). The productions of manics offer us more for discussion. Means of indicating rapid association are numerous. In *Plate 51* we see only a fraction of the productions of an Italian male of 38 in his third typical manic attack. In each figure we are able to recognize the original configuration, but it is quickly embellished with a flight of ornamentation. Unlike the schizophrenic individuals who make additions to the configuration, these do not destroy or distort the original figure but tend to embellish it or to emphasize it with additions which are secondary to the original design. If the drawer was not inhibited he rapidly covered pages with whirligig drawings suggested by his own flourishes, which are not reproduced here for lack of space

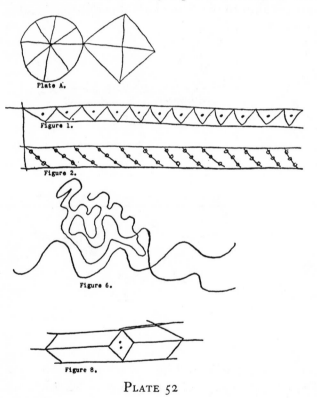

Plate A.

Figure 1.

Figure 2.

Figure 6.

Figure 8.

PLATE 52

ANNA C. (*See Plate 52*). Still another type of manic response is seen in *Plate 52*. This was produced by a woman of 27, suffering from her second manic attack. In each figure, she saw all the possible spatial relationships and immediately drew them into the design. It will be realized that these drawings in some way immediately express the optic imagery which was described by normal individuals in Chapter V. The lines also express the possibility of movement in the parts of the gestalten. It is as though the person is keenly aware of all the lines of force and movement in the optic field created by the stimulating configuration, but which are usually inhibited and not brought into consciousness.

E. F. Still another type of manic association is seen in the productions of a manic woman of 52 in her third attack. Her drawings are clumsily and poorly executed but in the process of making them she expressed, verbally, a rapid association which included many fields of visual, kinesthetic, emotional and social experience. Of Fig. A she said: "That is easy", but although she tried it four times, she succeeded finally only in a crude way after having finally neglected each unsuccessful trial, saying, "It is a ring and a diamond; my it is a beautiful ring, but it don't look as pretty as mine". Of Figs. 1 and 2 she said, passing on quickly from the one to the other, "Those are eyelets, embroidery; you have to punch them with your stylet; it is not so easy to make them all the same size, but the design isn't so pretty as the daisy and violets I used to make" (note the rhyming). Of Fig. 6 she said: "It is a snake walk and I bet you can't do it", and she began to move her feet about in preparation for a dance. Of Fig. 8 she said, "It is a house and lot and my mother owns it". The fact that this woman apparently found limitations in her ability to express her rapid associations in the drawings has led her to a quick verbal association which tended to express optic, auditory, but especially kinesthetic and emotional or personal experiences.

These visual motor gestalten in manic depressive individuals also express the instinctive difficulties in the pathologic state together with tendencies for inhibitions and relapses in perceptions and associations in the other perceptual or emotional fields.

CHAPTER XI

STANDARDIZATION OF THE GESTALT FUNCTION IN A PERFORMANCE TEST FOR CHILDREN

THE COPYING of these figures by children is a test which shows the maturation level of the child in the visual motor gestalt function. It appears from the studies in sensory aphasia (Chapter VII), that the visual motor gestalt function is a fundamental function associated with language ability and closely associated with various functions of intelligence such as visual perception, manual motor ability, memory, temporal and spatial concepts, and organization or representation.

Street has standardized a gestalt completion test. His aim was to help fill the need for a test which was "clear cut in structure and well-defined in nature", and to help clarify the confusion that has followed from empirical tests, when it is not clear what functions they are measuring. Street believed that his gestalt completion test measured a specific capacity that is probably involved in the perceptual process. He used a type of picture puzzle of familiar objects made up of black figures on a white background, or white figures on a black background: "by deletion, parts of each figure have been made to form the ground, so that in order to perceive the picture, it is necessary to complete the structure; that is, to bring about a 'closure' ". It appears that, in the first place, Street overlooked the motor phase of every perceptual function without which the gestalt function cannot be reckoned; and in the second place the deletions were arbitrary and often artificial, and not a functional part of the "gestalt".

With the help of Miss Anita Ruben (now Psychologist at the New Hampshire State Hospital), this test has been standardized on eight hundred school and nursery children. The children were tested in a suburban (Pelham) grade school, in two public day nurseries in New York City, and in the hospital wards and out-patient departments of the pediatric and psychiatric services of Bellevue City Hospital. Children three to eleven years, inclusive, were used, or children of preschool age and also those in the first to fifth grades, inclusive. Adult drawings were obtained from school teachers and members of the hospital staff. Children of three years and younger usually produced only a scribble, unless the figures were produced in front of them and they were allowed to imitate the motor acts. All of the figures are satisfactorily produced at the age of eleven years. Adults add only a certain motor perfection or perfection in detail in sizes and distances.

The test may, therefore, be considered of value as a maturation test of performance in the visual motor gestalt function between the ages of four and eleven—which is the age when language function including reading and writing are developing.

The maturation process has already been discussed in Chapter II. In this chapter, we are concerned with the standardization of the test.

Gesell has standardized the drawing ability of small children and finds that a child of nine months to one year can scribble imitatively; that a child of one to one and one-half years can scribble spontaneously; that a child of two years can imitate a vertical stroke; that at three years a child can copy a circle from a model; that at four years a child can copy a cross; that at five years, a square and a triangle; and that at five years a child can also draw a recognizable figure of a man. Gesell expressed wonder at the inability of a child to produce an oblique cross as early as it could produce a square cross, or a diamond as early as a square. He tried to explain it on the basis of a motor difficulty. It is quite clear from these studies, however, that the difficulty is related to the problem of visual motor gestalt function.

According to the Kuhlman standards, a child can make a mark with a pencil at one year, and copy a circle at two years.

Other workers are inclined to set the age for copying specific forms at a somewhat later stage than these two workers. In the Merrill-Palmer test for pre-school children, copying a circle is expected at three to three and one-half years and copying a square at three and one-half to four years. In the Stanford scale, a four year old child is expected to copy a square, a seven year old, a diamond, and a ten year old is expected to reproduce a more complicated design from memory. Charlotte Buehler finds that the four year old can reproduce a circle by imitation; that the five year old can reproduce schematic pictures such as trees, a man, etc., by imitation and that the six year old can reproduce a border made of a series of rings, triangles and crosses, around a paper.

From the standardization of the gestalt drawings we found that the three year old child usually responds with a scribble which is somewhat controlled; that is, the child stops spontaneously after making a small scribble on the paper before him, and repeats the same or similar response when each figure is shown to him.

The four year old uses circles and closed loops to represent some of the gestalt principles in all of the figures shown to him. Usually, Fig. A is two circles in the horizontal plane in the dextrad direction. Figure 1 is a series of larger or smaller circles, or loops, in the dextrad horizontal direction.

FIGURE A (*Plate 53*)

Description					Ages					
	(3)	(4)	(5)	(6)	(7)	(8)	(9)	(10)	(11)	Adult
Score 1. An inhibited scribble, i.e. drawing confined to a limited area on paper; the scribble similar to that for the other drawings presented.	20	4	1	—	—	—	—	—	—	—
Score 2. Scribble inhibited to such an extent that drawing resembles test form; two loops in the dextrad direction may be incompletely closed. Usually they do not touch, but sometimes they touch, overlap, or have considerable space between them. Frequently a line is drawn from one to the other. More than two is incorrect.	4	12	7	3	1	—	—	—	—	—
Score 3. Two closed loops in horizontal plane and dextrad direction; the second is modified so that it appears less like a round loop than the first and has features that make it resemble a square. The figures frequently overlap.	2	5	26	6	9	2	4	—	2	—
Score 4. First form a fairly good loop, the second a fairly good square, to the right of the loop. They may or may not touch.	—	3	8	3	—	2	1	—	—	1
Score 5. First form a fairly good loop, the second a fairly good square, to the right of the loop *and* the square is oriented on the diagonal. They may or may not touch.	—	2	4	7	5	4	5	1	—	—
Score 6. The loop and the square oriented on the diagonal, touch.	—	—	4	33	17	28	22	5	40	8
Score 7. "Perfection", i.e. the motor perfection of a good circle and a good square on the diagonal; diagonals of the square are about equal.	—	—	—	7	—	—	2	5	7	1

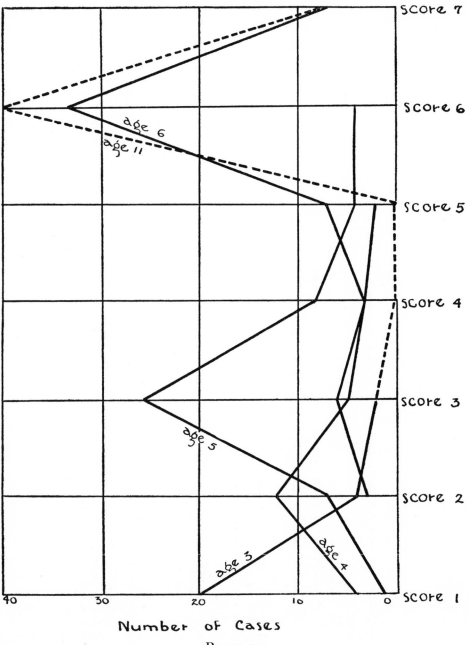

Number of Cases

PLATE 53

FIGURE 1 (*Plate 54*)

Description	(3)	(4)	(5)	(6)	(7)	(8)	(9)	(10)	(11)	Adult
					Ages					
Score 1. Inhibited scribble; for explanation see Table 1.	18	4	2	—	—	—	—	—	—	—
Score 2. Response indicates horizontal dextrad direction; any symbol may be used.	1	5	—	—	—	—	—	—	—	—
Score 3. Series of loops in the horizontal dextrad direction; sometimes there is indefinite perseveration; the number, size of loops, and distance apart varies. Reduplication of rows, vertical rows, or flourishes, are incorrect.	2	13	7	—	2	1	—	—	—	—
Score 4. Control of loops into very small loops or actual dots.	1	—	23	22	13	20	13	—	7	—
Score 5. Very small loops or dots; length of series resembles that of test form.	3	5	20	28	15	15	13	10	17	1
Score 6. Good dots, on straight line; length of series resembles that of test form; distance between dots similar to that on test form.	—	—	4	3	5	5	10	24	30	13
Score 7. In addition to above, pairing is present. The line need not begin and end with a remnant.	—	—	—	—	—	—	—	—	—	4

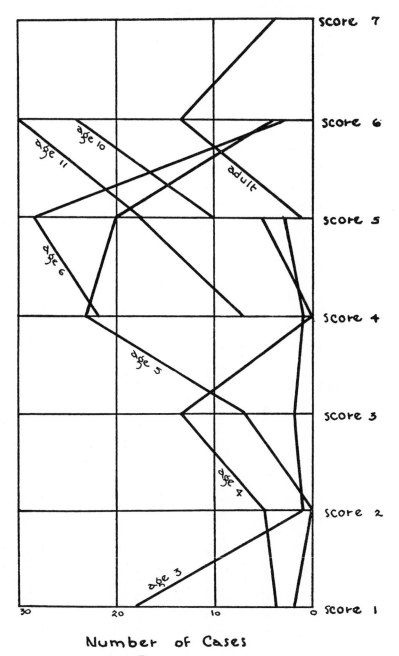

PLATE 54

FIGURE 2 (*Plate 55*)

Description		Ages								
	(3)	(4)	(5)	(6)	(7)	(8)	(9)	(10)	(11)	Adult
Score 1. Inhibited scribble; for description see Table 1.	20	3	5	—	—	—	—	—	—	—
Score 2. Single horizontal, or vertical, series of loops or a mass of loops.	2	18	18	2	5	4	—	—	—	—
Score 3. Fairly small loops in a horizontal series; the series is perseverated three or more times in the vertical direction; it may cover the whole page.	—	6	34	17	5	2	3	—	—	—
Score 4. Vertical rows of three small loops; the rows are perseverated two or more times in the horizontal direction; figure is likely to be uneven, but there is no attempt to slant the rows.	—	—	—	30	19	22	10	5	13	—
Score 5. Small good loops in a horizontal series of vertical rows of 3, *plus* an attempt to slant the first row and add the others so that the whole figure slants.	—	—	—	—	2	8	15	11	25	—
Score 6. A definite and successful slanting of each vertical row, keeping the whole figure horizontal.	—	—	—	3	4	4	10	10	21	5
Score 7. "Perfection", i.e. careful motor execution such that the loops are about the right size, distance, and relationship to each other; the number of loops either approximates the test form or is sufficient to express the principle.	—	—	—	1	1	—	—	5	3	12

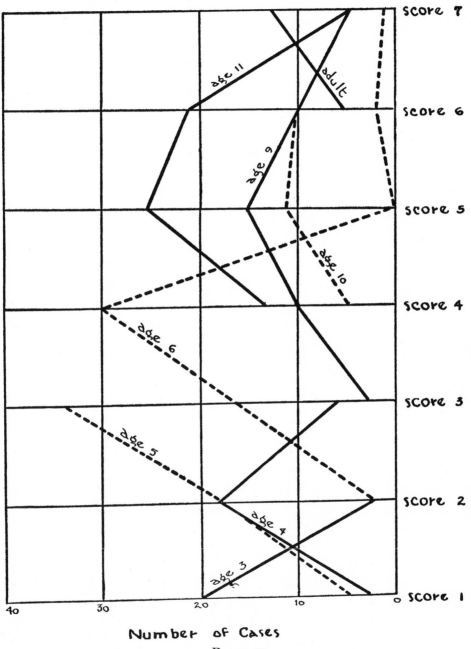

Number of Cases

PLATE 55

FIGURE 3 *(Plate 56)*

Description	(3)	(4)	(5)	(6)	(7)	Ages (8)	(9)	(10)	(11)	Adult
Score 1. Inhibited scribble; for description see Table 1.	17	5	2	—	—	—	—	—	—	—
Score 2. A mass of loops or dots.	—	11	10	4	3	1	1	—	—	—
Score 3. Dextrad series of loops.	1	6	13	2	3	1	1	—	—	—
Score 4. Single dot with a dextrad series of dotted *lines*; small loops may be made instead of dots; the lines get progressively longer; the number of lines and dots varies, but indefinite perseveration is not shown; distance between the lines varies. The series should not be in any direction but dextrad.	—	4	19	17	5	10	9	—	5	—
Score 5. Single dot with a dextrad series of dotted *arcs* of progressively larger size with more dots. The first two arcs in the series contain the correct number of dots, but in the last two the number is only approximated. The last two arcs may tend to become straight lines. (In a very few cases small loops are made instead of dots.) The number of arcs is the same as the test form.	—	—	8	25	15	19	18	9	17	—
Score 6. Single dot with a dextrad series of dotted *angles* of progressively larger size, with more dots. The last angle may tend to become arc shaped.	—	—	—	2	6	8	6	13	30	3
Score 7. "Perfection", i.e. careful motor execution with good dots properly spaced, accuracy in angle formations, and distance between angles approximating that of test form.	—	—	—	—	—	—	—	8	4	13
The following responses are not shown on the graphs.										
Score 1. A single loop or kite-like figure that resembles the external form of the figure as a whole.	1	—	—	—	—	1	—	—	—	—
Score 2. Figure perceived in two parts, one a single left handed dot and the other, a series of dotted (or looped) arcs or angles.	—	—	—	3	1	1	1	1	2	—

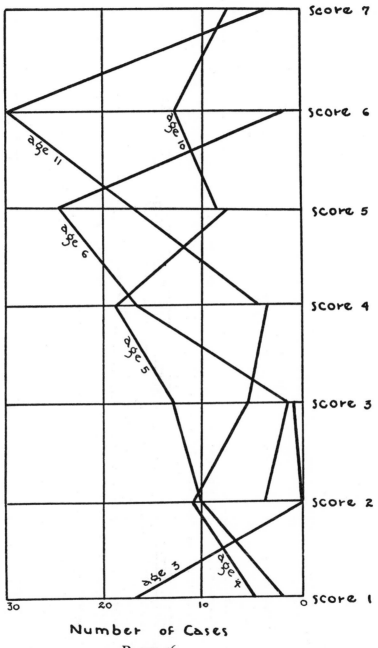

Number of Cases

PLATE 56

FIGURE 4 (*Plate 57*)

Description	Ages									
	(3)	(4)	(5)	(6)	(7)	(8)	(9)	(10)	(11)	Adult
Score 1. Inhibited scribble; for description see Table 1.	15	6	4	—	—	—	—	—	—	—
Score 2. Two dextrad loops; they may be closed or partially open; they may overlap, be adjacent, or have a distance between them.	5	10	6	—	—	—	—	—	—	—
Score 3. Two open loops, in dextrad formation; there may be an attempt to put the second a little lower than the first. There is some feature about them to distinguish one from the other, i.e. the first is more square or the second more open. In some cases the square is closed. The figures are adjacent or have a distance between them.	1	5	28	11	13	11	2	—	4	—
Score 4. The first figure is a good open square. There is an indication of an actual oblique relationship.	—	2	17	29	20	23	22	5	20	—
Score 5. "Perfection", i.e. motor coordination in size, shape, and relationship.	—	—	—	12	3	2	8	26	29	8

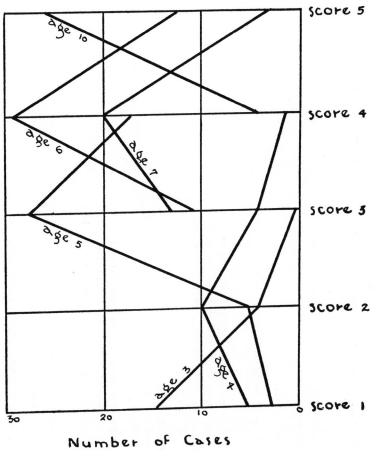

Number of Cases

PLATE 57

FIGURE 5 *(Plate 58)*

Description		Ages									
---	(3)	(4)	(5)	(6)	(7)	(8)	(9)	(10)	(11)	Adult
Score 1. Inhibited scribble; for description see Table 1.	17	5	—	—	—	—	—	—	—	—
Score 2. Mass or series of loops or dots.	—	5	6	—	—	—	—	—	—	—
Score 3. Wide open arc with dash; the figure is usually formed of loops but may be formed of lines.	2	13	10	6	3	—	1	—	—	—
Score 4. Arc with upward dash composed of very small loops, or less frequently, of dots; sometimes a combination of both loops and dots is made. An arc of only 3 dots with a dash drawn from the center one, is occasionally found. There is little orientation.	—	3	21	13	9	10	8	8	8	—
Score 5. Dotted arc resembling the test form in size. The dotted dash goes in the right handed, upward direction. There may be some disorientation in the clockwise direction.	—	—	10	25	21	24	19	6	15	—
Score 6. "Perfection", i.e. dotted arc half or a little more than half of a circle; the dotted dash more or less correctly placed. A little disorientation in the clock-wise direction is usually found. The number of dots is approximate.	—	—	4	7	2	3	7	21	35	8
The following responses are not shown on the graph.										
A large loop with a straight line dash.	1	—	3	1	—	—	1	—	—	—
Two parts: the first an open loop or dotted arc, the second a separate dash.	1	—	4	—	2	—	—	—	—	—

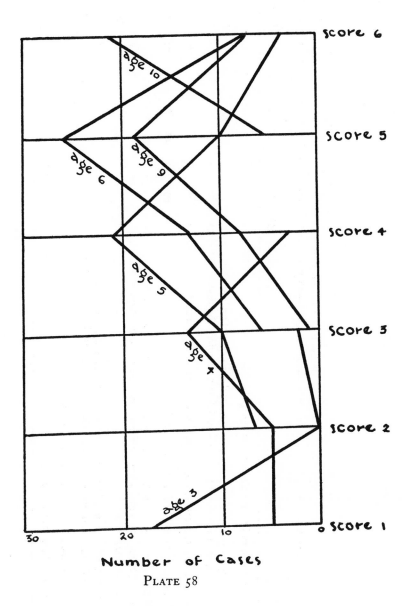

Number of Cases

PLATE 58

FIGURE 6 (*Plate 59*)

Description	(3)	(4)	(5)	(6)	Ages (7)	(8)	(9)	(10)	(11)	Adult
Score 1. Inhibited scribble; for description see Table 1.	18	4	3	—	—	—	—	—	—	—
Score 2. Drawing emphasizes the horizontal dextrad direction. The lines are wavy or straight; the second may be parallel or dextrad to the first.	2	15	10	—	—	—	—	—	—	—
Score 3. A more or less straight horizontal line crossed by another line.	—	5	2	1	1	1	—	—	—	—
Score 4. Two wavy lines crossing at right angles.	—	3	19	14	22	25	24	—	16	1
Score 5. Oblique angulation; such that the relative lengths of the line resemble the test form, the curves are uniform, and the oblique angle is more or less accurate.	—	1	—	—	9	12	11	—	30	3
Score 6. "Perfection", i.e. in addition to the above, the size of the curves in one line is different from the other, and resembles the test form.	—	—	—	—	—	—	—	—	4	3
The following response is not shown on the graph.										
Score 1. Two touching wavy angles.	—	—	13	36	1	—	3	30	10	1

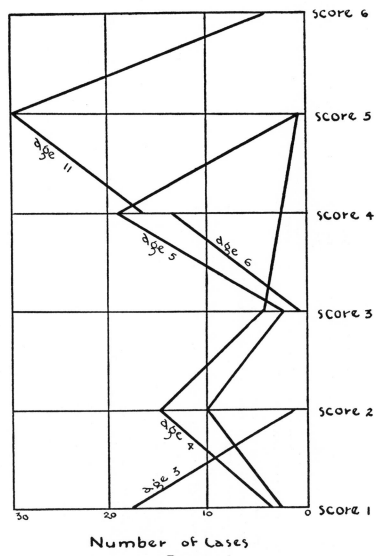

Number of Cases

PLATE 59

FIGURE 7 (Plate 60)

Description	Ages									
	(3)	(4)	(5)	(6)	(7)	(8)	(9)	(10)	(11)	Adult
Score 1. Inhibited scribble; for description see Table 1.	19	8	7	1	—	—	—	—	—	—
Score 2. Two loops that overlap, touch, or are separated. They are usually in the horizontal plane, but are occasionally placed one below the other. They should not be concentric.	1	17	15	3	7	4	3	—	—	—
Score 3. Two loop-like figures; there is a definite attempt to point the corners of the figures. Sometimes the corners are squared. They do not overlap.	1	2	20	16	5	9	10	3	3	—
Score 4. More or less good hexagonal forms which overlap. One figure is usually larger and differently shaped than the other.	—	1	6	29	15	19	16	3	15	—
Score 5. More or less good hexagonal forms. One figure may be larger and differently shaped than the other. There is a real *oblique* overlap.	—	—	—	4	7	8	5	16	33	1
Score 6. "Perfection", i.e. motor coordination in formation of good hexameters with one end more pointed than the other; there is a real oblique overlap. There may be some inequality in size.	—	—	—	—	—	—	2	5	11	9

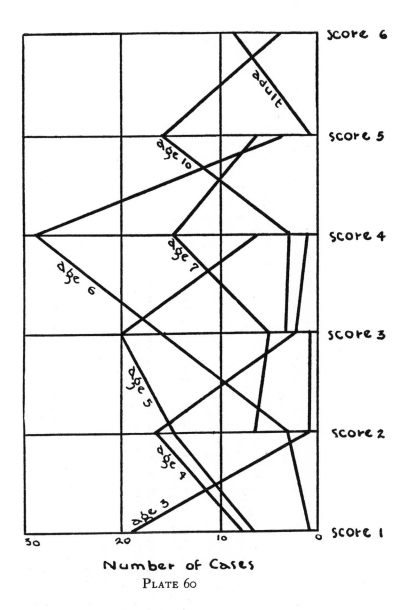

Number of Cases

PLATE 60

FIGURE 8 (*Plate 61*)

Description	(3)	(4)	(5)	(6)	Ages (7)	(8)	(9)	(10)	(11)	Adult
Score 1. Inhibited scribble; for description see Table 1.	18	—	5	—	—	—	—	—	—	—
Score 2. Two concentric loops, these loops may look just like those in Fig. 7 except that they are concentric.	2	13	7	1	—	—	—	—	—	—
Score 3. An attempt to elongate the first loop on the horizontal plane and place a smaller arc in the center.	—	6	22	4	3	—	1	—	—	—
Score 4. An elongated loop with more or less sharp corners, or two crossing arcs making the points at the ends, or more or less box shaped with 4, 5 or 6 corners. The inside figure may be a simple loop or better.	—	2	12	27	15	20	18	3	—	—
Score 5. More or less carefully formed hexameter with inside figure a fairly good diamond.	—	—	—	22	18	19	15	14	29	—
Score 6. Motor coordination of a good hexameter, with inside figure a good diamond. Size and relative positions resemble that of test form.	—	—	—	—	—	—	2	16	20	6

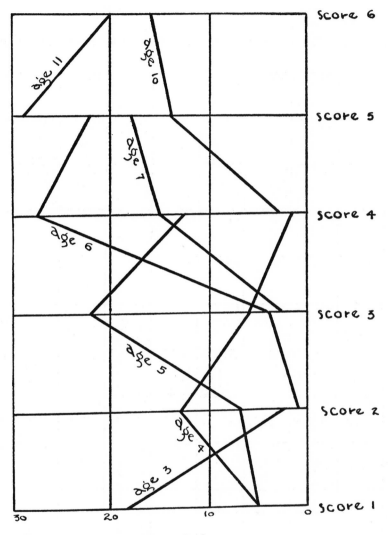

Number of Cases

PLATE 61

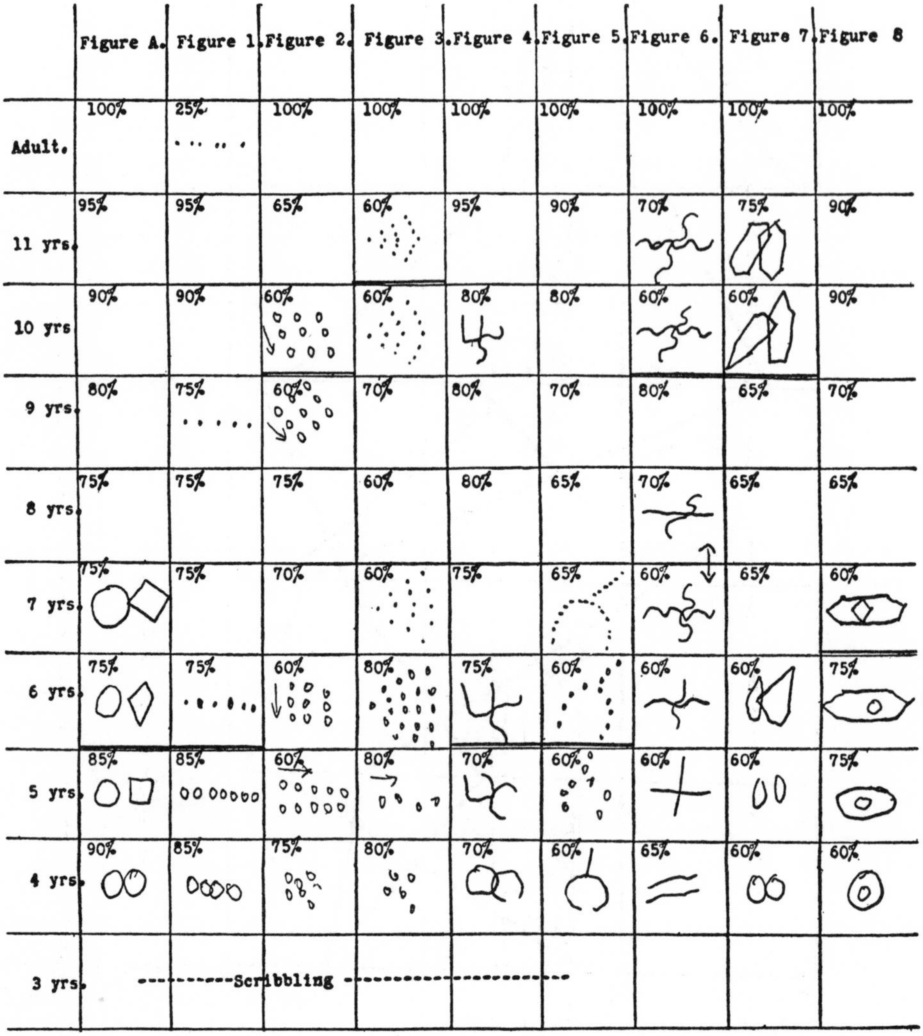

	Figure A.	Figure 1.	Figure 2.	Figure 3.	Figure 4.	Figure 5.	Figure 6.	Figure 7.	Figure 8
Adult.	100%	25%	100%	100%	100%	100%	100%	100%	100%
11 yrs.	95%	95%	65%	60%	95%	90%	70%	75%	90%
10 yrs	90%	90%	60%	60%	80%	80%	60%	60%	90%
9 yrs.	80%	75%	60%	70%	80%	70%	80%	65%	70%
8 yrs.	75%	75%	75%	60%	80%	65%	70%	65%	65%
7 yrs.	75%	75%	70%	60%	75%	65%	60%	65%	60%
6 yrs.	75%	75%	60%	80%	75%	60%	60%	60%	75%
5 yrs.	85%	85%	60%	80%	70%	60%	60%	60%	75%
4 yrs.	90%	85%	75%	80%	70%	60%	65%	60%	60%
3 yrs.	----------Scribbling -------------------								

PLATE 62

Figures 2 and 3 are masses of small circles. Figure 4 is two loops in a more or less horizontal direction, with, possibly, some effort to keep either or both circles partly open. Figure 5 is a partially open circle with a dash at the top. Figure 6 may be intertwining circles, or two horizontal unclosed lines, or segments of circles. Figure 7 is two dextrad circles and Fig. 8 is two concentric circles. At the age of four, therefore, the child may use closed circles or loops in horizontal dextrad, concentric, and mass relations. Dextrad horizontal direction may also be represented as a segment of a circle. Partially open circles are attempted. In other words, we may say that a four year old child can express form by loops or circles on a background; direction, by dextrad horizontals; numbers, by mass and perseveration; and to some extent these functions may be combined to produce integration in a pattern. There is a slight tendency to use open loops and segments of circles, but this is not consistent.

A five year old child may modify his circles and loops into closed square-like figures, or oblong oval figures or into open circles; he may use arcs of circles in various combinations, including perseveration of concentric arcs; and he may perseverate horizontal series in vertical direction and cross vertical and horizontal lines.

A six year old child may produce closed squares in the oblique direction; and represent oblique relationships by two partially closed loops, and by a segment of one loop in relation to another. He may also make circles so small that they are dots and represent points in space. It is possible, therefore, for him to reproduce Figs. A, 1, 4 and 5 correctly. He may also produce vertical series alone or by horizontal perseveration; or combine several of these functions in one figure so that he is not only able to cross lines but also to cross wavy lines. Another possible variation is to make Fig. 5 an open circle of small dots with an oblique dash at the top, etc.

The ages over seven add very little more than an improvement of obliquity and an increase in the numbers of combinations. Thus, in Fig. 2, the problem of forming an oblique vertical sequence of three small loops is a difficult one. Even after it is accomplished, the whole pattern tends to take the oblique direction indicated by this feature. This is often seen at the nine year level, and it usually requires a ten year old child to form a horizontal dextrad perseveration of oblique vertical sequences of three circles. An eleven year old child is required to form Fig. 3 as a horizontal dextrad series of obtuse angles of increasingly greater spread rather than the concentric arcs used at the younger ages. Only the unusual adult can notice the exact spatial relationships in the pairing of the dots in Fig. 1.

The charts and graphs show the standardization of the data. It is seen

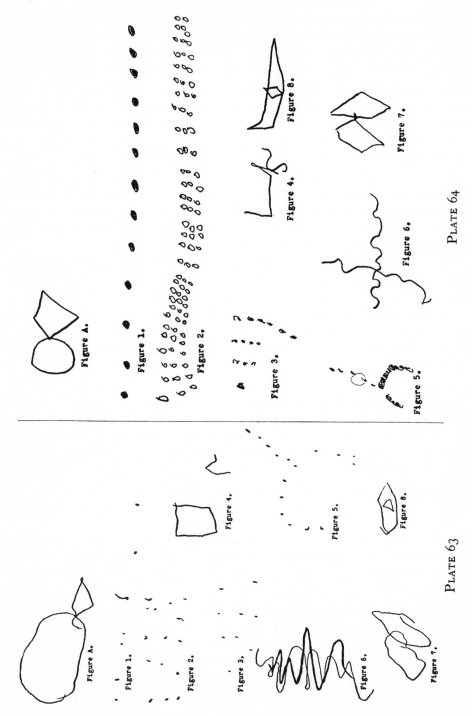

PLATE 64

PLATE 63

that Figs. A, 1, 4 and 5 are produced at six years; Fig. 8 at seven years; Fig. 6 at eight years; Figs. 2 and 7 at ten years; Fig. 3 at eleven years; and the pairing of dots in Fig. 1 by about one-third of adults.

Plate 62 is a summary chart showing type of responses at the different ages. The percentage of children who could do the type of response depicted or better is printed in the upper left-hand corner of each square. This chart may be used as a scale for determining the maturation level of any child or defective adult who may be asked to draw these figures. It is not of value for individuals whose mental level is above eleven years unless they present some type of mental disease that tends to distort the visual motor gestalt function such as are shown in the other chapters of this book.

The two following case histories are quoted to show the use of this test in the study of children:

ELIZABETH (*See Plate 63*) was four years and five months old when she was brought to the Mental Hygiene Clinic because of infantile behavior in the day nursery where her mother left her to go to work. She came from an Armenian home where Armenian was spoken. Her infantile behavior included poor toilet training, baby talk, restlessness and inattentiveness. On the Stanford Binet test she scored a mental age of four years and 0 months with an I.Q. of 91, but it was noted that her English was limited because of her bilingual home. On the Randall's Island Performance Test she scored a mental age of 6 years and 3 months with an I.Q. of 142%. She did not do well with the Goodenough test for drawing a man. She blocked on attempting the drawing and became restless and upset. The drawing could not be recognized. She spoke of the devil's eyes and the belly button. The gestalt drawings were performed as shown in *Plate 63*. Figure A scores at the five year level, being composed of a round closed loop with the second part of the figure modified to resemble a square. Figure 1 scores at the 6 year level; Fig. 2 between 6 and 8 years, Fig. 6 at 6 years; Fig. 4 at 6 years, except that the first part of the figure is closed; Fig. 5 at 6 years or above; Fig. 6 cannot score because her lines are not crossed and both are vertical although both are wavy lines; and Figs. 7 and 8 score at 6 years. After a period of treatment on the children's ward for her neurotic problems, she was able to produce a man without fears or inhibitions and scored over 6 years on the Goodenough scale. It thus appears that this child of four years had a mental age of six years. The gestalt tests were in keeping with the performance tests while the Stanford Test was performed at a disadvantage because of the language handicap.

JESSE (*See Plate 64*) was a colored boy of 11 years and 6 months. He was accomplishing nothing in school and had not learned to read. He was poorly supervised by a defective mother and beaten so much that he ran away from home. In the Stanford Binet Test he scored a mental age of 6 years and 0 months, with an I.Q. of 52. On the ward among other children his social adjustment seemed at a somewhat higher level. On the Pintner Patterson Performance Scale he scored a mental age of 7 years and 10 months with an I.Q. of 73. On the Goodenough score for drawing a man he scored 7 plus years. With the gestalt drawings seen in *Plate 64*, all his productions fell between the 7, 8 and 9 year level. Thus this child may be considered a mentally defective of the high grade moron level in actual ability, although he had not profited by his schooling, and on Stanford Test, which assumes school and language accomplished, he scored much lower.

CHAPTER XII

GESTALT FUNCTION IN MENTAL DEFECTIVENESS

MENTAL DEFECTIVENESS is not an entity; neither is it an isolated deficiency in intelligence. It is a symptom which may be associated with many different conditions. Although the general attitude towards mental defectiveness assumes that it is due to an actual quantitative failure in endowment or to loss of function through structural disturbance due to disease processes or injuries to the brain, there are some studies which point to a different evaluation. L. Pierce Clark defines mental deficiency as "the failure in the process of acquiring, absorbing and using knowledge for an adaptive mastery of reality". He points out that even where the defectiveness is associated with definite organic injury, there are dynamic or psychological factors that play a part, for as "any wound to the physical structure must be reflected in the ego's efficiency and in its sense of power to govern the total organism in its approach to reality". In other words, the reaction of the personality-as-a-whole in terms of the psychobiological unit must be considered. We must look upon defectiveness as a dynamic response even where there are structural defects. Viewing mental defectiveness in this way, we may look for impaired intellectual responses in association with various conditions and may, therefore, expect that a somewhat isolated specific function such as the visual motor gestalt function would show different types of disturbances in different types of conditions which are associated with mental defectiveness, and even that they might be more or less specific for different conditions.

A simple retardation in maturation processes with a constitutional or hereditary background will be the most obvious type. Such individuals would be expected to show the responses of a normal child of the same mental age. Specific developmental defects in the field of language might be expected to show disturbances akin to the aphasias resulting from disease processes or injuries to the brain. The conditions have been described and analyzed by Orton (Salmon Lectures). The congenital word blindness, or congenital alexia, are the best known of this group, and within recent years children with this type of disability are recognized, studied and given remedial training which helps them to compensate for their specific deficiency. Such children do not show any disturbance in the visual motor gestalt function. Children with congenital aphasia are more difficult to differentiate from the general category of mental defectiveness because of the speech retardation and the necessity to utilize special performance tests to show the general intellectual level. Other aphasic disturbances secondary to structural injuries may be present with difficulties in the symbol unit and with perseverative tendencies. Such a case will be discussed. Schizophrenia in children or some similar condition may be more common than is generally realized but is not differentiated from other children who are functioning at a mental defective level. According to Potter, institutions for mental defectives probably care for many such children who are not recognized as such. Difficulties in perception or in impulses may also be important factors either with inhibited impulses or hyperkinesis. Confusional difficulties with disorientation, with essential difficulties in spatial orientation of configuration on the background, may occur with epilepsy or other conditions. The problem of temporal disturbances, which is recognized as a difficulty in mental deficiency, has not been adequately studied. Neurotic or emotional blocking of speech and social contacts, and infantile reactions is known to be a factor in apparent retardation of development where there is no structural or functional disturbance in the realm of perception, memory, ideation, judgment or reasoning. In others, the retardation seems to be specific for certain fields with normal or superior ability in other fields. Some children rated as mentally defective by the standard tests and social criteria are able to handle the visual motor gestalten in a normal or superior fashion.

There is some tendency still expressed by some psychologists to look upon mental defectiveness as a simple quantitative problem. According to Pintner he recommends the percentage criteria which he believes would divest feeblemindedness of sociological criteria. Thus ($1\frac{1}{2}$ according to Burt) the lowest X percentage of the community should be considered as feebleminded. He also believes that clinical classification has no value except for those medically inclined. This would be true if the only basis for the classification was on the size of the head, anatomical structure of the brain, endocrine features and body build. But if it is true that classification will also indicate different intellectual and psychic functions with the possibility of different types of training, the classification would seem to be of value to the psychologist, psychiatrist and educators as well.

Mental defectiveness has been studied by the Rorschach test both by its original author and by Beck (See Chapter XII). It has been stated that the feebleminded react to the blot configuration with the fewest number of whole responses. The number of whole responses is considered by Rorschach to be an indicator of the energy which is directed towards associational activity and, also, of a conscious or unconscious will to complex achievement. It is thus concluded that whole responses are a function of intelligence. Other functions of intelligence as measured by the Rorschach test are listed by Beck as perception of sharp forms, inner creativity, originality and a low percentage of stereotyped thought. Alfred Binet has also defined feebleminded persons as "stereotyped children". Beck also reports that he found a typical reactions in 11%—some of which suggested the dissociative phenomena of schizophrenia and others, an unevenness in the maturation processes.

A dynamic theory for feeblemindedness has been offered by Lewin who belongs to the Wertheimer-Köhler-Koffka school of gestalt psychology, but who has directed his studies mostly in the field of personality and will. He finds that the feebleminded are to be characterized as dynamically more rigid and less mobile. He bases this on studies on feebleminded children's psychical satiation, resumption of interrupted action and substitute values of substitute actions. Thus, when children are given a task and interrupted in the middle to carry out another task to completion, 79% of normal children will return to complete the uncompleted task, while 100% of feebleminded children will invariably return to the original task. When a substitute task is offered for the uncompleted task, it is found that in normal children that a high substitute value (returning to incompleted task reduced from 79 to 33%) may be obtained, but again, in the defective children, the rigidity of the tensions system reveals itself by the low substitute value (94% returned to incompleted task). Thus the will of the feebleminded child is said to be strong and rigid. Lewin also quotes Eliasberg to the effect that the feebleminded think more concretely and perceptually. It is also said that the feebleminded child shows less "stratification", meaning that a feebleminded child of a given age shows less differentiation than a normal child of the same age brought up under similar circumstances. The question still remains, however, as to whether he really resembles a younger normal child. On this point the author would disagree with Lewin and show the evidence that indicates that the defective child may be more or less rigid and less differently differentiated than the normal younger child of a similar mental level, as defined by the usual standard tests.

We are now interested to see how mentally defective individuals will respond to these visual motor patterns. We find that we do not get simply a lower level of the integrated gestalt production commensurate with the mental level determined by the other standard tests. There is a much greater variety of productions among mentally defectives of a given mental age level than among normal children of the same mental age. There is,

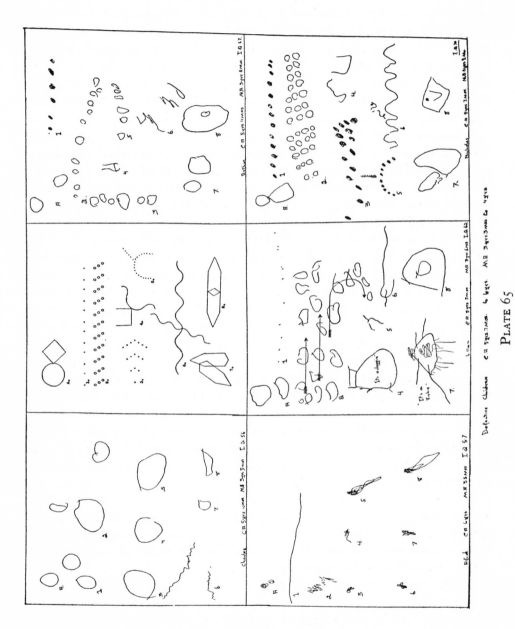

PLATE 65

of course, retardation of some one or all of the various maturation processes, but this retardation may be more in one field than in another. Of
course, one sometimes gets results which are commensurate with the mental level and sometimes one may get results above the mental level indicated by the standard mental tests or by the poor social adjustment that
may justify the institutional care. This is partly due to the fact that this
is not a test of educational or language accomplishment but of maturation processes and is, in that way, more comparable to the so-called performance tests. Often the gestalten are produced in a more simple fashion
but with better motor control. There may be more primitive scribbling
but in some way it is better controlled as the work of Alfred (*Plate 65*)
will show. In *Plate 65*, all of the children were of about the same chronological and mental age but it will be seen that the productions vary
greatly. Besides the scribbling of Alfred we see how Charles uses the primitive loop almost entirely—but with what seems to be a greater conservation of energy and with less tendency to experiment than the younger
normal children display. Arthur shows a combination of the scribbling
and the loops. Often the results are somewhat bizarre and show dissociative features that are suggestive of some process akin to schizophrenia,
such as we see in the work of Nicholas. Figures A, 1 and 5 are as they
might be done by a bright younger child, while all of the other figures
show some mature features with more or less dissociation, scattering, re-
duplication, etc. In some defective children we find hyperkinetic features.
Lillian had suffered from encephalitis and had a defective intelligence
quotient. She was hyperkinetic in all her behavior. The hyperkinetic
features in her productions are seen in the tendencies to flight in Fig. 2
where the third line is tailed off around in a curved fashion, in Fig. 4,
where both open figures are closed and by a rapid association that she
called "doggie", and in Fig. 7, which is only partially finished when her
flight carries her off into much decoration by perseveration, and c she
called "fishie". In a similar way, Fig. 5 (which is not reproduced) was
turned into a "duckie". Aside from the hyperkinetic features, however,
her productions show the characteristics of her retarded mental level,
rather than of her chronological age, as may be seen in the horizontal
series in Fig. 2.

For defective adults with a mental age of about 3 years I wish to refer
to the papers I have already published of patients that I studied in the
Springfield State Hospital of Maryland (*Plate 66*). The same principle of
expressing all implied gestalt relationships with the primitive loop is seen.
The primitive dextrad horizontal directional features are prominent. Per-

severation is more prominent than in children. Dots are always seen as loops and fragmentation and separation of parts occurs frequently. The immature child's difficulty with crossed lines and all oblique and slanting relationships persists.

Mental defectives with a mental age of 4 to 5 years (*Plate 66*) show many of the same gestalt features of normal children of the same mental age with some better motor control of the simple looped figure. Series or masses of this enclosed loop is a prominent feature. Perseveration is poorly controlled, as in the work of Antonio. At the same time, figures are often smaller than they are in normal children and sometimes there seems to be a paucity of impulses, as in the case of John. Adults with a mental age of 4 to 5 years and an I.Q. of 25 to 30% use very simple means to express relationships, though the most primitive forms of the implied pattern are nearly always present in some way—if they are not lost in the perseverative tendencies. Thus, Sadie interprets the first five figures as either shorter or longer series or masses of loops or dashes (for dots). She crosses some of these dashes in Fig. 6; modifies this response and perseverates it for Fig. 7; modifies it again for Fig. 8 but fails to put the little figure inside the big, being apparently carried away by the dextrad horizontal directional tendency. Perseveration is the prominent and disturbing feature throughout. Oresto, however, does not perseverate, and his work might be taken for that of a child of 4 years who had good motor control. The same may be said of Abe.

Through the courtesy of Dr. Poull, a number of mental defective individuals at the Children's Hospital of Randall's Island were tested with this gestalt test. Individuals were chosen whose mental age ranged from 3 to 6 years. Otherwise, the cases were unselected. Fifty-six individuals were tested, there being thirty children from 4 years and 2 months to ten years and 3 months, and twenty-six adults from sixteen to forty-nine years of age. The results of these examinations have been analyzed (1) to determine if the maturation level could be estimated in the light of the standardized results of the tests on normal children; (2) to determine if the results were comparable to the mental test obtained by the usual standard tests (Terman in this group of cases); (3) to determine if the test revealed a simple retardation in maturation in the visual motor gestalt in defective individuals, or gave evidence of other types of disturbance.

Ten children had a mental age at the three year level. Their chronological age ranged from 4 years 2 months to 7 years, their I.Q. from 48 to 72%. In six of these the child responded to each test figure with a simple unformed scribble which could not be analyzed further than to say that there was no evidence of any maturation of the visual motor gestalt function above the third year level. One of the children produced drawings decidedly superior to the level indicated by the standard tests and the social criteria. This was a child of 5 years and 7 months with an I.Q. of 70 (See Nicholas, *Plate 65*). The productions were such as would be expected of his actual age or a year better, except that he also showed some tendency to separate parts and split figures in the schizoid fashion. Three other children produced drawings which could be recognized as efforts to draw the test figures. In many ways they resembled the drawings of a 4 year old child except that they were more restrained; the unit figure was more rigidly utilized and perseverated in two; and there was some dissociative phenomena in the third.

Twelve children had a mental age at the fourth year level. Their chronological age was 5 years and 9 months to 8 years and 9 months and their I.Q. ranged from 53 to 80%. Two of these children produced drawings normal for their chronological age, one other showed drawings appropriate to his chronological age but with some confusional features due to disorienting the figures on the background. Three children showed a simple retardation in maturation processes so that the drawings were more or less appropriate for the mental age given by the standard tests. Three children showed retardation in the maturation process with perseverative or aphasic disturbances. One showed retardation with confusional features, and one showed retardation with dissociative or schizoid phenomena.

Five children had a mental age at the fifth year. Two of these produced drawings at a maturation level that was normal for their chronological age but one showed schizoid and the other aphasic phenomena; two children showed a simple retardation of the maturation of the process at the mental level indicated by the standard tests while one showed retardation with asphasic features.

Three children with a mental age at the six year level showed one with normal drawings, one with retarded drawings and one with aphasic drawings. The children examined included intelligence quotients between 48 and 80 or, in other words, the moron range. Six of the thirty children were still too young and their drawings too poorly differentiated to be of analytical value; they may possibly have represented a simple retardation. Otherwise, there were six children whose drawings indicated a simple retardation of the maturation process for the visual motor gestalt function in keeping with other intellectual tests. Six children produced drawings

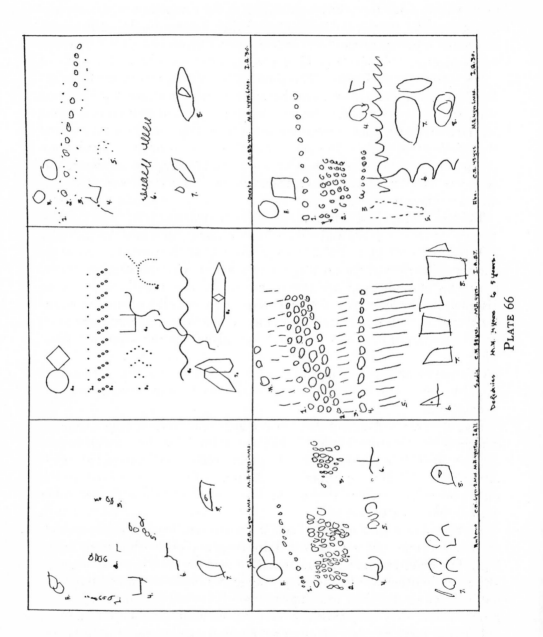

PLATE 66

at the maturation level of their physical age with evidences of disturbances which might be characterized as aphasic due to simplification of the gestalt unit with perseveration; confusional features due to disorientation on the background; or schizoid features due to dissociative phenomena.

Of the adults, nine had a mental age at the fifth year level with an I.Q. ranging from 27 to 31. In none of these did the drawings show the features of a simple retardation to the mental age of four. Two, however, rather closely resembled the work of a four year old child, except for the poverty of the drawings which may be interpreted as a poverty or blocking of impulses. Three others showed this same poverty of responses which were also distorted and might be considered to be a combination of perceptive and impulse disturbances. Three others showed marked aphasic disturbances and the remaining one showed schizoid disturbances. Fifteen adults had a mental age of 5 with intelligence quotients ranging from 33 to 39. One drawing was that of a normal child. Four showed retardation to the mental age of five years but with the usual defective features of restricted activity, rigidity of response and some slight but recognizable disturbances in the way of disorientation or perseveration; seven showed marked aphasic disturbances and three showed marked schizoid features. Two adults, with a mental age of 6 and with I.Q. of 40 and 41, showed aphasic phenomena.

This group of adults showed a range of intelligence quotient from 27 to 41; thus they represented the imbecile group. It is interesting that one individual produced a normal adult drawing. Of the others only six at the most produced drawings which could be interpreted as a simple retardation in maturation to the mental age as estimated by the other standard test. Even in these, there were features which are considered typical of the mental defective intelligence. All of the others showed more or less severe disturbances which we have found as characteristic in known cases of aphasia, schizophrenia or confusional states, or disturbances due to blocking of impulses and severe perceptive defects. It would appear, therefore, that in the lower grade defectives a considerable number of the individuals show some specific type of disturbance which might be comparable to the specific disorders in the speech centers of the brain; or to dissociative phenomena which are associated with schizophrenia; or to specific impulse or perceptive disorders; or to confusional features, which may accompany a number of different organic conditions.

It will be of considerable interest to more carefully analyze individual cases where the differential diagnosis represents a challenging problem.

JACK (*See Plate 67*) was a child who suffered speech disturbances in connection with convulsions. He was 8 years old when last examined. He was apparently born a normal child in a gifted family. At the age of two he began to show precocious ability in piano playing and was considered a prodigy by the family. However, following a severe attack of whooping cough, he developed epileptic convulsions of the Jacksonian type. The treatment was neglected as the mother was unwilling to recognize the condition. His mental development was retarded with the fre-

PLATE 67   PLATE 68

quent severe convulsions. Following a particularly severe series of convulsions he became paralytic on the right side and aphasic. The mother then consented to treatment. Luminol and ketogenic controlled the convulsions, the child recovering from the aphasia and paralysis, except for some weakness in the right hand. His behavior improved. However, his mental condition remained retarded at 50 on the Stanford Binet scale. He had lost considerable of his ability at the piano. His gestalt drawings (*Plate 67*) show many of the features of a child of 5 to 6 years of age with the tendency to rigidity in response and poverty in impulse often seen in the defective. There is some perseveration seen in Figs. 4 and 7 and a poor attention to detail. There are no marked disturbances which may be characterized as aphasic at this time, however.

WALTER (*See Plate 68*). Another child who was brought to us with speech difficulties was Walter. He reported to the Mental Hygiene Clinic at intervals between the ages of four and six because of retardation in speech and dull inadequate social behavior. He was an illegitimate colored child of an uneducated colored mother. A marked discrepancy between the Stanford Binet test and the performance tests was noted at the time of the first examination. When he was 4 years and 5 months old, his intelligence quotient on the Stanford Binet test was 68 while on the Randall's Island performance test it was 83. When he was 5 years and 11 months of age the intelligence quotient was 79 on the Stanford Binet and 110 on the Pintner Patterson performance test. The history showed that he had not learned to speak until he was nearly four and that then his speech was stammering and could be understood only by his mother. He was shy, quiet and unresponsive to strangers and his mother assumed an over-protective attitude. Even when he was nearly six he would not speak for strangers. The mother claimed that he played and talked with children, but usually only repeated what they said. She claimed that his speech was adequate for her to understand his wants. Under observation it was gradually possible for his teachers to adapt him to situations so that he would speak. His speech was always normal, but very limited. He seemed to have to learn new items of speech either as words, phrases or sentences, with considerable conscious effort. Some observers felt that his speech was inhibited on a neurotic basis. There is some evidence against this, however. The mother gave the history that he had preferred the left hand but she had taught him to use the right. At the time he was under observation, it was very difficult to determine his dominant hand or his dominant eye. He seemed to shift from one to the other side. It was noted, however, that when he used his right hand in writing numbers or copying, he was inclined to produce reversals or mirror images. His gestalt drawings are very significant (*Plate 68*). They are not the drawings of a normal six year old child who might be neurotically inhibited. They show striking features similar to the adult aphasic. The looped unit symbol is used with many variations and with perseverative tendencies. Difficulties in interpreting the figures are also seen. These features are combined with features which suggest normal mentality. Figure A, for example, shows the diamond formation of a six year old child. Figure 6 represents a similar level of attainment. It was thus our opinion that this child was suffering from a congenital aphasia, associated with disturbances in cortical dominance together with perceptual difficulties. The unit symbol of loops are used in Figs. 1, 2, 3, 5 and 6, while square formations were used in Figs. 4, 7 and 8, all of which are not reproduced because of lack of space.

MARTIN (*See Plate 69*) presented another type of problem. He was brought to Bellevue Hospital at the age of 6 years because of peculiar behavior, which had been progressing since the age of four years. He lived in a fantasy world of his own; it was not possible to make contact

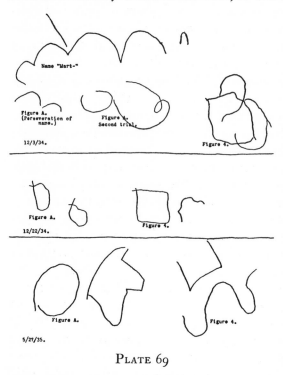

with him and his speech which at first was very scanty, consisted of inappropriate ejaculations which were not related to the environment. He had a dreamy, far-away look; he would not keep his clothes on; he had to be fed. The diagnosis of schizophrenia was suggested from the beginning but, because of the rarity of this condition in children, it was questioned. Some believed he was a mentally defective child suffering from some emotional shock. There was gradually some improvement and the first ascertained psychometric gave him an intelligence quotient of 74. In the course of a year his improvement was striking and he was able to score an intelligence quotient of 95. By this time, few doubted that he was a case of schizophrenia. Although he has been home and attending school for nearly a year, it is still evident to psychiatrists that he is still showing behavior typical of schizophrenia. His teachers consider him a high grade mental defective, as he does not attend to his lessons or accomplish anything. He is always preoccupied with his fantasies. At the time when his intelligence quotient scored 74, there was noted a marked scattering in the responses, and many atypical ones. Also, his gestalt drawings (*Plate 69*) at that time (12-3-'34) showed his tendency to use a symbol for his name, and to perseverate it inappropriately in response to Fig. A. His Fig. 4 is a closed square with an inadequately formed loop overlapping it. Some time later (12-22-'34), his drawings more nearly resemble the test forms but there is considerable separation of parts and use of closed forms

PLATE 69

for open ones. Six months later, when his I.Q. was 95, his drawings show evidence of adequate intelligence, but with some bizarre features.

The study of the visual motor gestalt function shows that the problem of mental deficiency is not a simple one. If we were to assume a slow-up or simplification of the maturation process in a unified way, we would expect less differentiation, a more unified system, a stronger and simpler gestalt, such as we find in the younger normal child. This does occur in some individuals, especially among the higher grade defectives. Such individuals seem to represent usually the hereditary constitutional defective. Even in these cases, we do not find a simple retardation in all of the principles of the integrated visual motor gestalt function. Motor control is usually better than in normal children of the younger age. Small, energy conserving figures are the rule. The primitive loop is freely used with less motor play or experimentation. The patterns are more rigid. In the majority of the responses of all the mental defectives investigated other features are also seen. It must be realized that many individuals who function as mental defectives do so not because of a hereditary retardation in maturation, but because they are constitutional deviates of some other sort; or because of some subsequent brain pathology. It is, therefore, possible to get every sort of deviation in the personality reaction and in the gestalt function. Detailed analysis leads to the conclusion that many individuals who are functioning as mental defectives show evidence in their gestalt drawings of more or less severe aphasic disturbances which are characterized by the use of a perseverated primitive symbolic unit while others show the dissociative phenomena characteristic of schizophrenia; and still others show disturbances in impulses with a poverty of response or hyperkinetic features; and finally, others show perceptive difficulties, confusional features, with disorientation of whole figures or parts of the figures, on the background. Such analysis leads us to the opinion that there are multiple causes of mental defectiveness, which may be classified as (1) simple retardation in maturation; (2) specific disabilities in the fields of language; (3) dissociative phenomena which distort the whole personality; (4) impulse disturbances; (5) perceptual disturbances; (6) confusional disturbances. Such an analysis leads one to the hope for a better understanding of mental defectiveness and the hope of classifying and treating specifically some groups. Furthermore, the gestalt test aids in the analysis, differential diagnosis, and prognosis of specific cases.

CHAPTER XIII

THE GESTALT FUNCTION IN MALINGERING AND IN THE GANSER SYNDROME

It is not easy to simulate a malinger. Schilder in the foreword to Larson's book on Lying and Its Detection, states that it is a human necessity to respond truthfully to the perception of a situation; the world of reality has to be respected. Even when human beings lie with their consciousness, they tell the truth with their unconscious. It is very interesting to note the efforts to distort the gestalt drawings under different conditions. Physicians, nurses and medical students were assigned to the task of drawing the gestalt figures as though they were defectives. In other instances the drawings were submitted to prisoners who had been or were being tried for some crimes and who appeared to be simulating a psychosis, or who presented a Ganser syndrome. It will be evident that none of these individuals was successful in neglecting the essential gestalt principles which their maturation level would make it possible for them to experience. At the same time, each simulator modified the drawings in a way that proved to be typical for the individual. In every case, therefore, our end result was the "gestalt" of the stimulation, the situation and the individual.

Physicians, medical students, and nurses, who were not acquainted with the principles of the work on the gestalt function, were asked to draw the picture, assuming either that they were mental defectives or that they were in a situation where they were tried to pretend that they were mental defectives and not able to draw the figures in the correct way. *Plate 70* shows the drawings of a physician. He attempted to make his lines hazy and indefinite but, in every instance, the gestalt principles were exactly indicated. The drawing of oblique lines, diamond shaped figures, and oblique relations and angles which is the best evidence of adequate intelligence, is in every instance reproduced. The only deviation from the stimulus is in Fig. 4 where the open figure is closed, but closed as a square. If the low grade mentality were to use a closed symbol for this figure, he would use a closed loop. The final point of interest is that in the effort to inhibit the intelligence, the simulator has succeeded only in inhibiting his impulses so that the drawings are small and inhibited. This tendency will be noted to some extent in all conscious simulators.

In *Plate 70*, a different type of response is shown by a nurse. The symbols are all simplified somewhat as an aphasic does them, but there is none of the perseveration of the aphasic. Furthermore, the simplification of the symbol has, in every instance, strengthened the gestalt principle involved. Superficially, this might appear to be a rather successful attempt at simulating a mental defective response with aphasic features. Most strikingly it will be noted, however, that slanting relationships are well performed as in Figs. 2, 4, 5, 6 and 7.

Another effort of a physician is shown in *Plate 71.* Again we see the small inhibited figures with a tendency to simplify the symbols and

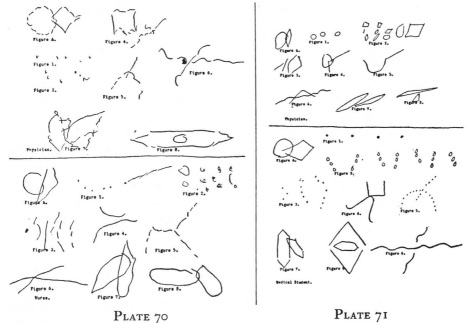

PLATE 70   PLATE 71

strengthen the gestalt. Furthermore, there is an effort to make details bizarre but in so doing the high intelligence level of the simulator is revealed. Thus in Fig. 2 the small loop is replaced by the sophisticated square and diamond. There are some instances of displacing or disorienting details which will be discussed in connection with the next drawing.

Plate 71 shows the drawings of a medical student. Here we see features which may be characterized as Ganser in type. First, it must be pointed out, however, that the figures were all well drawn and in every instance the principle of the gestalt is well shown. Oblique relationships and diamond figures are clearly shown, showing the native good intelligence. Where the figures are distorted it is accomplished by changing the relationships or direction of details. This could be done only by first perceiving the correct gestalt and changing a detail secondarily. In other words, it is the approximate answer but not the correct answer; but is approximate only because the correct answer is known. Thus, in Fig. 2, every other vertical line is placed in an oblique position opposite to that indicated, and a similar effect is shown in Fig. 3. In Fig. 4, the two parts are connected at opposite corners. In Fig. 8, the small inside diamond is made the large outside figure. In Figs. A and 5, the parts are made to overlap, while one is fragmented, in Fig. 6, to prevent overlapping—although it is clear that the individual is capable of crossing lines in Figs. A and 5. In this individual the effort to simulate has called out certain unconscious mechanisms which aid them in distorting the figures, although all of the mature gestalt principles remain intact. It thus appears that true simulation is impossible—although changing the test by adding a new situation to it modifies the results by bringing out tendencies to inhibit the impulses, simplify the symbols and to strengthen the gestalt; and that in certain individuals who possess a Ganser tendency, uncon-

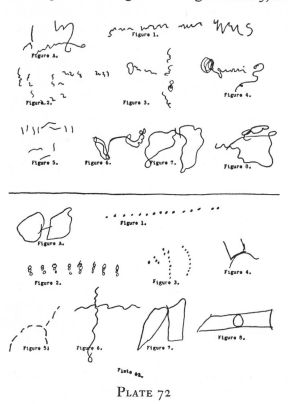

PLATE 72

scious mechanisms result in approximate (often opposite) responses when the actual details are recognized. It is not possible, however, to break down the actual experience of the essential gestalt principles which are inherent in the biological system.

We might expect, however, that where the motivation for simulation was much stronger, where, for example, evidence for mental unsoundness would save an individual from a life term or even the death sentence because of a crime for which he is being accused, that simulation might be more successful.

Plate 72 shows the drawings of an 18 year old colored boy who was facing his fourth charge and therefore a very long sentence if he were convicted. He had been advised by fellow prisoners to pretend that he was crazy. He was seen on the ward waving his arms about his head and declaring that there was a host of black angels flying around in the air and, upon seeing the physician, declared that she was the queen of the black angels. His drawing of the gestalt figures at that time showed a lot of hazy, wavy lines fairly similar to the physician's in *Plate 70*. Here they are more bizarre, however, and indicate that parts or details are misplaced and disoriented similar to the medical student in *Plate 71*. Possibly it is hard to be sure that Fig. A resembles the test figure, but Fig. 1 is quite satisfactory, and Fig. 2 is made up of wavy lines representing each unit of three loops, but scattered about. Others may be analyzed similarly. Figure 7 shows the boy's actual ability. These drawings are best understood by comparing them with this same boy's drawings a few days later—when he had given up his effort at malingering and did the best he could. The standard psychometric tests at that time showed that he had a mental age of 7-6 and an intelligence quotient of 47 on the 16 year basis. His gestalt drawings are in keeping with his mental age; Fig. 7 in his simulated drawings indicates this mental age. Thus, his simulated drawings show that he is a mental defective, and they do not resemble any of the psychoses or abnormal mental states which have been studied. This boy was a simple, superficial confessed simulator.

A more serious problem now arises among the so-called Ganser syndromes. Many prisoners show reactive emotional states following the commission of a serious crime and the facing of trial and punishment. It must be realized, however, that many emotional, complex-determined, and neurotic trends are stirred by such experiences. Besides, there is also the problem of why the individual committed the crime and, in many cases, there must be an assumption of a preceding abnormal state of mind. Bleuler (Textbook) has stated that Ganser syndromes occur as a reactive state in schizophrenics who must face an impossible situation. Such a case has been reported by me in my studies of mothers who murder their children. A mother who had shown schizophrenic trends since the birth of her child choked it to death at the age of three years. She had a severe reaction in which she was at first depressed, then in a Ganser state and finally in a stupor. This is not an uncommon course for such individuals to take. It does not seem necessary for an individual to be schizophrenic to pass through such a reaction. Other inadequate neurotic, hysterical, or psychopathic individuals may do the same. The Ganser syndrome is characterized by bizarre and inappropriate answers to even the simplest questions. However, the answers are usually approximately correct. It is as though the individual, having heard the question, used it as an association test and gave the association word as an answer. This requires that the actual answer must be inhibited and that a related word or idea is offered instead. In many cases it appears that this phenomena is not deliberate, conscious lying or malingering, but an unconscious mechanism which is the result of a pathological emotional state in the individual. Glueck classifies malingering into three groups, stating that there is the malingering of the frankly insane, of the apparently mentally normal, and the borderline group who may be potentially normal, but verging on psychosis. He states that a person may be obviously insane and malingering, and that, as such, it is a morbid symptom. Let us consider two case histories.

R. S. (*See Plate 73*) was a 46 year old colored man who was charged with manslaughter in the first degree for killing his wife while drunk.

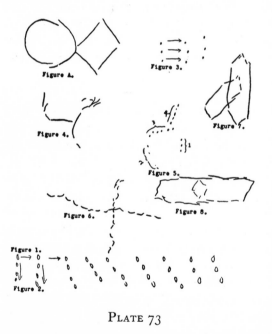

PLATE 73

He claimed confusion for what had happened. He said that there had been a quarrel over money. She had been saving money to send him back to the West Indies because of his excessive drinking habit in this country. He had demanded the money. In the quarrel, she had come towards him with a knife, and he didn't know what happened until the next day when he found that they were both in the hospital suffering from knife wounds from which she subsequently died. He said he must have done it unconsciously. He was depressed and retarded. When he got a little better, he complained of his head and said he could not sleep. He said that he thought something worried his brain. He claimed that he had been discharged from the army as mentally unfit. He said that he heard the doctor's voice at night and that he had heard other voices for two years. However, he had been in the hospital two or three months before, for alcoholism, and there was no evidence of such symptoms.

His response to the standard psychometric tests was slow and laborious, but he made a dull normal score in some tests. There were some Ganser-like responses. He said that a rat and mouse had five legs and that a green desk blotter was blue.

In this case one must consider the possibility of alcoholic toxic and depressive features and the tendency to exaggerate or utilize both and other mechanisms, as well as a partial malingering response.

The drawing of the gestalt figure (*Plate 73*) shows that he is not defective. This was also the opinion of the psychologist as a result of his incomplete responses to the standard psychometric tests. There are some unusual responses. It was noted that he was very slow in performing the test. There was a tendency for fragmentation. This was more apparent on watching him perform the test. Figures 5 and 6 for instance, were made in small units and put together, finally, into a complete and correct gestalt. In Figs. 1, 2, 3 and 4 there are some confusional features. In this case we are, therefore, inclined to say that the man is not defective, but that his drawings show some confusional, depressive and Ganser features. These conclusions are also in keeping with the case history.

L. K. (*See Plate 74*) was a colored vaudeville actor of 21 years. He was arrested on a charge of panhandling. All his responses to examinations were very silly and absurd and all of his answers to questions were inappropriate although approximations to the correct answers. At times, however, he split words and sentences so as to make himself almost unintelligible and at other times he used "baby talk". He said that a dictionary was a Bible; a newspaper he called a geography; he called a notebook a pocketbook; and he called the doctor a Sunday-school teacher. When asked to pick up the inkwell, he picked up the blue card next to it; and when asked to point to his tongue he took out his penis and pointed to it. He called the hospital Belmont Hotel and said that he had been there twelve years when he had been there twelve days. His behavior on the wards was appropriate for eating, sleeping, toilet habits, dressing, etc., but otherwise he was dull and uninterested. He once told a nurse that he had come to New York City from another city because he could get more relief money here. A psychometric test was motivated by the psychologist advising him that it was necessary to find out how smart he was before he could leave the hospital. His answers were appropriate and a mental age of 9.2

with an intelligence quotient of 62 was obtained. After several weeks of such behavior this man was sent to a state hospital as insane. The charge against him was a minor one and not sufficient to motivate such a behavior consciously. Nevertheless, his behavior was in every way typical of a prisoner's psychosis of the Ganser type.

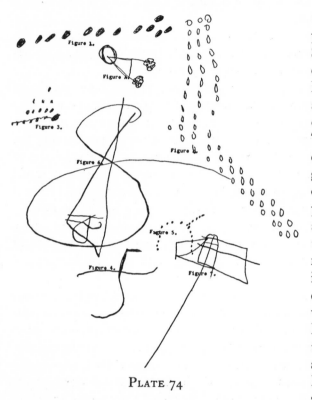

His gestalt drawings (*Plate 74*) show many pathological features. Some figures are disoriented in space; notably Figs. 2, 3, 4 and 8. There are confabulations in the case of Figs. 2, 6 and 7. These are of a nature to distort or destroy the gestalt rather than flights of fantasy, however. The peculiar turning of Fig. 2 also has the characteristics of a dissociated phenomena. Finally, one is inclined to look upon his drawings as dissociated with an inferior capacity. It is, therefore, likely that in this case we must accept the experience of Bleuler that a Ganser syndrome points to a schizophrenia in a person who has suffered some intolerable experience. In the state hospital he acted in the same nonsensical manner, but at times he was apparently able to answer coherently. He gave the history that, previous to his psychosis, he had been homosexual in his interests and often impersonated women, both on the stage and for the sake of his male lovers. He has remained in the state hospital more than a year at this time, showing more severe symptoms, claiming that he was immaculately conceived, and was the second Christ.

PLATE 74

CHAPTER XIV

THE PSYCHONEUROSES

WE DO NOT EXPECT to find disturbances in perception or in the visual motor gestalt function in the psychoneuroses. In these conditions we find disturbances in the normal emotional development through the infantile stages. The child who is thwarted or over-indulged in his demands for satisfactions arising from his relationship to his mother or father or his own bodily needs will tend to show a persistent demand for the same type of satisfactions. Since the reason for the thwarting or over-indulgence occurs in the infantile stage when consciousness is not fully developed, it usually happens that the individual throughout his life may be unconscious of this reason—unless it can be brought into consciousness by some special method such as psychoanalysis. The unacceptable infantile demand for satisfaction is usually represented by some other activity which stands as a symbol for the real desires and drives of the personality. Since the stage of dawning consciousness is also the stage of maturation of the perceptual or perceptual motor gestalten, it would not be surprising to find that some such gestalten might become the symbol of the individual's unsatisfied infantile drives. In other words, they might represent the individual preoccupations, obsessions or compulsions. The following case history is representative.

BILLY (*See Plate 75*) has been under psychiatric observation in the Bellevue Hospital and Mental Hygiene Clinic for a year. He was five and a half years old when he first came. He is a child of superior intelligence, the only child of parents of college training. His home life has not always been satisfactory as his parents have not been entirely compatible and several times the mother has gone home with Billy because of jealousy, sexual incompatability, or so-called nervous breakdowns. The birth was difficult since the mother had a narrow pelvis and instruments were needed. It is probable that Billy has heard this discussed in his presence. There was no evidence that his head was injured at the time of birth, however. He was born with an imperforated anus which was operated on the second day after his birth. The function of this sphincter was impaired and he had to have dilatations of the anus, both by the finger of his mother almost daily, and by instruments of physicians from time to time up until the age of two, and at intervals after that. The normal course of his oedipus complex was interfered with because of the relationship between the mother and father and the frequent visits of the mother and the child away from home. He openly expressed a hatred of the father, the desire for his death or removal from the home, and the wish to have the mother to himself. He further identified himself so much with his mother that he expressed a strong dislike for his penis. He wished to be like his mother; he wanted to sit down to urinate; he often denied his penis. The more detailed elaboration of his emotional problems in this respect will not be given here as they do not concern us especially. At the age of two and a half years, when he was visiting with his mother in the home of his grandparents he enjoyed the pleasure of automobile rides as many children do. He was fascinated by the stop and go lights and seemed to believe that they made the cars stop and go. At this time at home he would play in a little cupboard where he could sit on a shelf and close himself in by a door like the door on an automobile. He would take imaginary rides with imaginary stop and go lights to make the car stop and go. He then became interested in doors as such and with their door knobs, key holes and hinges and, finally, with the door checks. Door checks became an obsession with him which occupied him from this time up to the time he came to the hospital for treatment. He was preoccupied all day with doors and door checks. He was rejected from kindergarten because he smashed the fingers of the other children in the doors. He could not play on the streets because he could not be stopped from playing with the neighbors' doors all up and down the street. He was much concerned with

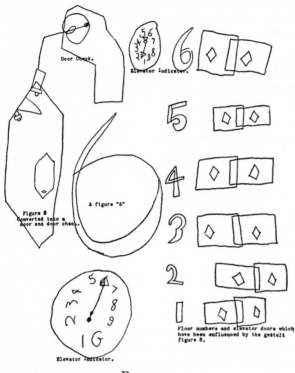

PLATE 75

the shapes of the doors, the doorknobs, and casements and hinges. The opening and closing of the doors would occupy him for hours. He was especially fascinated with door checks. All of his questions were concerned with how doors open and close. He believed that the door check made the door open and close. He believed that other openings were regulated in a similar way by door checks. Thus when told by his mother about how babies were made inside of the mother's uterus, he believed that they got out by means of the door check. He would also occupy himself by the hour in drawing doors with door checks. He valued these very highly and became extremely aggressive if an effort were made to remove them from him or to destroy them. It was highly important in the making of these doors that they maintain certain proportions and that the shape of the plate for the key-hole and the doorknob, the hinges and the hinge plates bear a definite relationship to the shape of the door. Thus they must all be square or rectangular so that the long axis was up and down. If they were drawn for him so that the long axis was vertical it disturbed him to the point of a rage. Furthermore, the colors of the crayons were important. Green doors and door checks were especially valuable as they represented "Go" while red ones represented "Stop". So far we can see in this child, he is very much concerned with movement and the impetus for movement; for openings and the mechanisms of openings—and he is concerned with symbols for these things. When he deals with them as visual motor patterns, he demands that they conform to his concepts of such patterns and he treasures such patterns very highly. After he was on the Children's Ward for a month he returned home and came frequently to the Mental Hygiene Clinic for Psychotherapy (by Dr. Paul Schilder). During this time he developed some new obsessions. He resented his placement in the hospital away from his mother and was very greatly preoccupied with the reasons for sending him there, and with his new experiences and associates there. An effort had been made to direct his good intelligence into the lines that usually interest a child of his mental age. He was taught his numbers and how to read. He was greatly preoccupied with the numbers, and especially with the number 6. This was the number of the floor on which the Children's Ward is located. Much of the day was spent in the schoolrooms and playrooms of the roof or eighth floor. On returning to the ward by the elevator it was the habit of Billy to watch the mechanisms of the elevator, and especially a slit in the wall of the elevator whereby the elevator mechanic could determine the number of the floor. This 6 was a large, open-faced figure. It was this 6 which fascinated Billy for a long time. He seemed to think that it indi-

cated the arriving at and leaving of the ward. For months he was preoccupied with this number as formerly he had been occupied with door
checks. He made *6's* with paper, crayon, and clay all day long. He experimented with all kinds of 6's and noted all their characteristics. He compared other numbers to 6. Thus he said he liked 6 best of all because it
was an open or smiling number. He liked 8 least of all because it was all
closed up and sad. Next to 6 he liked 2 and 5. He also liked 6 because it
had an edge on one side of it, but he hated 1 because it was all edge. He
didn't like 7 because it was almost like 1. He said that 9 was a 6 upside
down, but was not much interested in it. Due to his increasing aggressive-
ness under treatment (which cannot be discussed in this limited discussion) he was returned to the ward about eight months after his first admission. On this occasion he became obsessed with the indicators over
the elevator doors which indicate the presence of the elevator and the
direction in which it is moving. These indicators were round in form with
a clocklike face and nine numbers, and, as it happened, with 6 at the top.
At the time he had first learned his numbers he had shown some passing
interest in the clock with its numbers and moving hands. The elevator
indicator, however, fascinated him completely. He believed that the indicator made the elevator come and go. He believed that the numbers on
the indicator regulated the numbers on the floor and, since 6 was at the
top, he had reason to believe that all of the floors in the hospital centered
about this important floor. He was occupied all day long with the spatial
problems of the series of floors from one to nine, and the circular series
of numbers on the indicator with 6 at the top. To complete these preoccupations, he was also obsessed with the doors on the elevators. These were
sliding doors with a little window in each of two partitions so that when
the doors were wide open by sliding on each other, the little windows were
parallel. He thus was soon able to preoccupy himself with nine sliding
pairs of doors with nine indicators each with the complete series of numbers on their face and always with 6 at the top. Now, it must be realized
that he has been occupied with the philosophy of space, of sequence, and
therefore of time, of movements and the mechanism of movement, of
doors and means of openings, of symbols for all these things and, by
this time 6 probably represented himself. It is also a feminine number,
not being penis-shaped like 1. It is also a smiling and open number,
not completely closed like 8. At home he often made 6's with clay or
paper and crayon and gave them to his mother as a precious gift. He could
not be induced to give them to his father although by this time he was
on fairly friendly terms with his father. It is not possible for us to say

what are all the mechanisms that relate these preoccupations with his personal experiences, with the difficulties with his anal sphincter, his hatred of his father and his own masculinity. It is of interest to note, however, how all of his optic imagery and visual motor patterns which constituted his favorite playthings conform to the principles of gestalten as laid down in this book. It is obvious how much he is concerned with the primitive closed figures and with closures in the more active sense. His preoccupation with the different numbers concerns itself with their gestalt. Often, in playing with the figure 6, he would state that one must close the lower part tight in drawing it on paper as that made it whiter in the inside. It is a well known phenomenon of the gestalt psychologists that the figure on a background determined by an outline has internal organization and really is experienced as whiter or more solid.

It was very difficult to concentrate Billy's attention on anything except his obsessions. Therefore, it was difficult to get him to draw the gestalt figures. On one occasion, however, he drew them as well as an average seven year old child. At other times he became distracted by some other figure that reminded him of his favorite preoccupations. Figure A, for example, would remind him of indicators, and he would draw them to the exclusion of everything else. Figure 1 would remind him of sequences and he would begin writing numbers that indicated the floors of the hospital. Figure 7 was joined together by door checks; Fig. 8 on one occasion was turned into a door and a door check added; at another time, the figure was used to indicate the sliding doors of the elevator. *Plate 75* shows a few of Billy's drawings.

Let us consider this boy from the point of view of Lewin, who claims that the structure of the mind is composed of psychical systems, stratums and spheres in different degrees of tensions, striving for equilibrium. It is possible to artificially create and experiment with a psychical tension system by requesting of a child that he start a task and then discontinue it for another task, which is continued to the point of satiation. It was found by Köpke that 79% of 7–8 year old normal children would resume the uncompleted task. It is also possible to measure the psychical satiation of normal children. Thus Karsten ordered children of 8 to 9 years to draw moon faces until they had had enough of it. The normal child of this age drew moon faces for 55 minutes and then drew figures of his own choice for 3 minutes more. It is hard to compare Billy with these experiments, since he is of younger age and because his restlessness, poor attention and resistance to comply with requests. It must be considered that he is in a constant psychic tension state in regard to his obsessional interests. It was thought that it would be of interest to try to determine his satiation point and to utilize the mechanism as a possible therapeutic measure. At the time when his interest in 6's seemed to be at its height he was given large pieces of wrapping paper and, to his surprise, requested to draw all the 6's that he wanted to. He drew 6's for fifty minutes with apparent satisfaction. Once he stopped to draw an indicator which was half completed before the examiner noticed it and requested him to set it aside and draw more 6's. He continued as requested and during the last five minutes became very restless and began to draw large 6's to fill the space more rapidly. He finally begged to stop. When he was offered the elevator indicator to finish he did not wish to do so. The next day, on entering the office, he requested, on seeing the paper and pencils set out: "Can I draw some other number today"? He was told to draw what he liked just so he continued to draw the same thing for the whole time. He drew elevator indicators but drew very large ones to fill up the large roll of paper given to him. This continued for some period and although he got very restless during the period and found many excuses to stop and had to be watched to keep him at the task, he always resumed it the next day with satisfaction. It appeared, however, that he had had more interest in many other subjects and had kept at the usual routine of the other children; shown more interest in the puppet shows and, in the art class when offered paper and pencil, drew other objects, on one occasion even drawing a picture of a car going to a festival, driven by his psychotherapist—this being the first evidence of an expression of a positive transference for his psychotherapist.

Similar problems occur in adults suffering from psychoneurosis, although the preoccupation with optic pictures is not so easy to determine as in this child when they constituted his favorite playthings—and the symbolic value is often more deeply hidden in the adult.

C. S. was a male of thirty years, a high school graduate. He had many obsessions and compulsions which interfered with the normal course of his life and made him feel very ashamed and inadequate. Only those which concern this problem will be mentioned here. Whenever he touches one side of any person or object, he must also touch the other side, or something awful will happen to him such as sickness or death. If he has a package to put on the table, he must put it in the middle of the table or something will happen. In this problem he identifies himself with the table and feels that if the package on the table does not balance the table, he himself will be underbalanced on one side and something will happen to the underbalanced side of himself. He has had this compulsion since the age of five years. At that age he had to place his head in the middle of the pillow and touch it in the middle, or he would be likely to get a hole in his head and sicken and die. We see from this hint that the obsessions and compulsions in this individual arose in the infantile stage and represented some fear of integrity to his body and thwarting of conviction of security and love. Numbers have values for him, also; number 1 stood for his father; 2 for his mother; 3 for his immediate family; 4 for himself; 5 for death; 6 for other persons; and 7 for objects. He is especially fearful of death and its symbols, and uses magic methods to weaken the threat of the symbols. If he sees a hearse, he will walk all around it so that he can see every part and so that no part should be unseen and all parts should be symmetrical within him. Also, if he touches his analyst by accident, he touches all sides of him so that no side will remain untouched. He also has dreams in which girls hold symmetrical positions, with black dresses and white collars, and form a circle that means sex. This gives him a mental reaction of satisfaction. We see that this individual tends to project himself, or his problems into the compact enclosed, balanced pattern. He may thus insure his own doubtful safety, well-being and satisfaction by maintaining their compactness, wholeness, and balance of these configurations.

F. R. was a 21 year old Italian lad with some high school education. He was subject to episodes of hypochondriacal depression when he suffered from depersonalization with unreality feelings both in regard to his body and his mind. He read about such things in the encyclopedia and believed that he was getting dementia praecox because he found his symptoms so striking. He complained that his body no longer seemed real nor his own and that neither did his mind. It is not possible to report all of his complaints, but only those that concern us here. He said from time to time over a period of five months, "I have no existence. I don't sleep well. I don't feel as if my body was my own. I never get a complete thought, I have no emotions. One day I felt a snapping in my head. After that I felt like there was a gap in the middle of my head and in my brain. The gap has been getting bigger and bigger and pretty soon there will be no brain left. . . . My brains feel like an empty space, now. Everything is dark; I can't visualize. I cannot have any mental pictures of anything I cannot do it. For instance, I cannot visualize any part of my home, or my sister or the face of my girl. I can never get the whole picture. I get only part of it for a fraction and then it disappears before I can get the rest of it". He was asked to imagine a white straight line and said, "I can't imagine it; it comes and goes". He was asked to imagine an interrupted line. "I can't do it; the interruption takes up the whole line and there is nothing left". He was asked to imagine a circle. "I can't get anything. It is all dark". He was asked to imagine the face of his girl: "I get a portion at one time and another portion at another time; I can't get it all at once. . . . Take the visualization of things—I can't do it right. I don't see it in its normal size. I see it as a miniature. A grown person looks about two inches. . . . There is a groove in the top of my head, getting larger and larger. My brain is split into two parts. Something broke when I first got my breakdown. I can't visualize. I can't see myself getting well. I can't feel any emotion. My girl almost got hit by a car but I don't feel anything". . . . "The groove in my head is getting larger, it is spreading, it is all dark in there; it is like an empty basket—there is no form . . . By all this conflict I am so beaten that my brain is flattened out like a pancake. I visualize my brain as though it were reduced to one-half the size of my skull . . . I can't think when you want me to. It is like my mind was a merry-go-round without any stops. My mind is blank and hollow. . . . When I try to visualize, the figure spreads all over the room. It has no form. For instance, if I try to picture my home or my automobile, I can't picture it so that it seems real. I only see parts of it . . . When I try to picture things they go round and round until they disperse". This boy also complained of the unreality of his body. He complained that he could not keep track of his limbs; that his arm was always some place else than he expected and that the distance to the top of his head was different from the way he felt it. He complained that with his left eye he could see the end of his nose too clearly and that it got detached from his face. But in all these phenomena we see natural psychological problems. If one lets one's self become conscious of it, one can see one's nose more clearly on one side and it does appear detached from the face. How is one to determine where one's limbs are or where the top of one's head is without looking or feeling for it continually? These are problems which Schilder has dealt with in his recent book *The Image and Appearance of the Human Body*: At the present, we are more concerned with his complaint that he could not visualize. When asked to visualize a circle he complained that he could not because it dispersed into space or whirled around too fast, and that everything was dark, or that he could see only bits of it at a time. This we know from our studies in optic imagery are the characteristics of optic imagery. In this boy they have become conscious phenomena. Only it is to be noted that he never complained of not being able to see circles and lines if he were not asked. He only complained of not being able to see the image of his home, the face of his sister, or girl, or his automobile. These were all parts of a very serious conflict in which he was caught but which cannot be described in detail here. Schilder, in his book mentioned above, states that symptoms of depersonalization occur at some stage in nearly every neurosis, with complaints of change in perception concerning the outside world and changes in experiencing their own body. It occurs in organs and functions which have the greatest erotic significance. One has reason to think that this boy who could never come to any decision in regard to marrying his girl had always enjoyed his erotic experiences by fantasy, and that these fantasies had been much intermingled with conflicts over his mother who had died a few years before, his stepmother whom he always resented, his older sister and his girl. However, Schilder states that it is "especially remarkable that the estrangement concerning the outside world is often an estrangement in the optic sphere especially" which he believes is due to the enormous importance of the optic element in the construction of the body image. This is particularly clear in this boy who continually associated his difficulty with the groove in the top of his head which occurred at the time something snapped in his head and left his brain dead and his mind a blank. Interestingly enough, it was possible to analyze the origin of this concept. As a small boy, as early as he could remember, it was the custom of his mother to shave his head in the summer to keep him cool. His head was so formed that there was a groove in the middle for which he was always tormented and which made him feel much ashamed and caused him to hide himself and withdraw from the family circle. His only compensation was to wet the bed at night because that brought his mother to his bed to give him special attention. Thus we see how these problems are all interwoven in the personal problems of the individual. On the third occasion of his depersonalization, the splitting of the head was brought about by the fact that his ambivalence and inability to decide to marry his girl led him to go to a prostitute where he acquired gonorrhea. Schilder defines depersonalization as the "characteristic picture which occurs when the individual does not dare to place his libido either in the outside world or in his own body". In this case it results in destroying the optic images by driving them back to their matrix which is the optic field with its whirling mass of movement and darkness, so that a clear meaningful gestalten in its background can no longer be experienced.

BIBLIOGRAPHY AND INDEX

BIBLIOGRAPHY

AMENT, W. The Mind of the Child. London, Kegan Paul, Trench, Trubner & Co. Ltd. 1926.

BALDWIN, J. Mental Development. The Macmillan Co., New York, 1903.

BECK, S. J. The Rorschach Test and Personality Diagnosis, 1, Feeblemindedness. Am. J. of Psych. 10; (July) 1930, 19.

BENDER, L. Principles of Gestalt in Copied Form in Mentally Defective and Schizophrenic Persons. Arch. of Neur. & Psych. 28; (March) 1932. 661.

———— Gestalt Principles in the Sidewalk Drawings and Games of Children. The Ped. Seminary and Jour. of Gen. Psych. 41; (Sept.) 1932, 192.

———— Gestalt Function in Mental Defect. Proceedings of the 57th Annual Session of the Amer. Assoc. of Mental Deficiency. 1933.

———— Disturbances in Visuomotor Gestalt Function in Organic Brain Diseases Associated with Sensory Aphasia. Arch. of Neur. & Psych. 30; (Sept.) 1933, 514.

———— Gestalt Function in Visual Motor Patterns in Organic Disease of the Brain Including Dementia Paralytica, Alcoholic Psychoses, Traumatic Psychoses and Acute Confusional States. Arch. of Neur. and Psych. 33; (Feb.) 1935, 300.

BENDER, L. and SCHILDER, P. Streuung und Reihenverminderung im sensiblen Abbau. Deutsche Ztschr. f. Nervenh. 129: 146, 1933.

———— and SCHILDER, P. Encephalopathia Alcoholica. Arch. of Neur. & Psych. 29, (May) 1933, 990.

———— and SCHILDER, P. Form as a Principle in the Play of Children. Pedagogical Seminary and Jour. of Genetic Psychology. 49; 1936, 254.

———— CURRAN, F. and SCHILDER, P. The Organization of Memory Traces in Korsakoff's Syndrome. Arch. of Neur. & Psych. 39; 1938, 482.

———— Psychiatric Mechanisms in Child Murderers. Jour. of Nerv. & Ment. Dis. 80, 1934, 32.

BENNETT, A. E. and HUNT, H. B. Traumatic Encephalitis. Arch. of Surg. 26; 397 (March) 1933.

BROMBERG, W. and SCHILDER, P. On Tactile Imagination and Tactile Aftereffects. Jour. of Nerv. & Ment. Dis. 76, pp. 1 and 133, 1932.

BROMBERG, W. Tactual Perception in Alcoholism. Arch. of Neur. & Psych. 28; 37 (July) 1932.

———— Marihuana Intoxication. Am. J. of Psych. 91; 303 (Sept.) 1934.

Bühler, K. and Volkelt, H. Die Neue Psychologie. Ztsch. f. Psychol. 1926, 99, 145–154.

Burt, Cyril. The Young Delinquent. Appleton, New York. 1925.

Child, C. M. The Origin and Development of the Nervous System. Univ. of Chicago Press, Chicago, 1921, pp. 114–115.

Clark, Leon Pierce. The Nature and Treatment of Amentia. Bailliere, Tindall and Cox, London, 1933.

Curran, F. and Schilder, P. Experiments in Repetition and Recall. Jour. of Genetic Psych. 1937; 51, 163.

Eddington, A. S. The Nature of the Physical World. The Macmillan Co., New York. 1929.

Gaupp, R. Psychologie des Kindes. Leipzig, B. G. Teubner. 1928.

Gelb, A. and Goldstein, K. Psychologische Analysen hirnpathologischer Fälle auf Grund von Untersuchungen Hirnverletzter, Ztschr. f. Psychol. u. Physiol. d. Sinnesorg. (I. Abt.) 83, 1920.

———— —— ———— Zur Psychologie des optischen Wahrnehmungs und Erkennungsvorganges. Ztschr. f. d. ges. Neurol. u. Psych. 41, 1918.

Gerstmann, J. and Schilder, P. Zur Frage der Mikrographie, Ztschr. f. d. ges. Neurol. u. Psych. 67; 59, 1921.
Mikrographie bei Sensorisch-Aphasischen. Arch. f. Psychiatrie. 74; 150, 1925.

Gesell, A. The Mental Growth of the Preschool Child. New York. Macmillan. 1924.

Glueck, B. Quoted by Larson, J. A. Lying and Its Detection. Univ. of Chicago Press, Chicago, 1932.

Goodenough, F. L. Measurement of Intelligence by Drawing. Yonkers, New York, World Book Co. 1926.

Hartman, G. W. Gestalt Psychology. Ronald Press Co., N. Y., 1935.

Head, Henry. Hughlings Jackson on Aphasias and Kindred Disorders of Speech. Brain 38: 1, 1915.

———— Aphasias and Kindred Disorders of Speech. The Macmillan Co., New York, 1926.

Hoch, A. and Kirby, G. H. A Clinical Study of Psychoses Characterized by Distressed Perplexity. Arch. of Neur. & Psych. 1; 1919.

Holmes, G. and Horrax, G. Disturbances of Spatial Orientation and Visual Attention, With Loss of Stereoscopic Vision. Arch. of Neur. & Psychiat. 1: 375 (April) 1919.

ISAACS, SUSAN. Social Development in Young Children. Harcourt Brace & Co., New York, 1933.

JAENSCH, E. R. Ueber den Aufbau der Wahrnehmungswelt. Leipzig, 1927.

KANNER, L. and SCHILDER, P. Movement in Optic Imagery. Jour. of Nerv. & Ment. Dis. 1930, 72, 489–517.

KATZ, D. Der Aufbau der Tastwelt. Ztsch. f. Psych. 1925, ergbd. 11, p. 77.

KLEIN, MELANIE. Psychoanalysis of Children, W. W. Norton & Co. Inc., New York, 1932.

KÖHLER, W. As Aspect of Gestalt Psychology. In "Psychologies of 1925", ed. by C. Murchison, Worcester, Mass. pp. 163–198.

———— Some Tasks of Gestalt Psychology. In "Psychologies of 1930", ed. by C. Murchison, Worcester, Mass. pp. 143–160.

———— The Mentality of Apes. Harcourt Brace & Co., New York, 1927.

———— Gestalt Psychology. Horace Liveright, Inc., New York, 1929.

KOFFKA, K. Perception, an Introduction to Gestalt Theories. Psychol. Bull. 19; 1922, 148.

———— Mental Development, in "Psychologies of 1925", ed. by C. Murchison, Worcester, Mass. pp. 129–143.

———— The Growth of the Mind. Harcourt, Brace & Co., N. Y. 1928.

———— Some Problems of Space Perception. In "Psychologies of 1930", ed. by C. Murchison, Worcester, Mass. pp. 161–187.

———— Principles of Gestalt Psychology. Harcourt, Brace and Co., New York. 1935.

KRAEPELIN, E. General Paralysis, Monograph 14. New York, Nervous and Ment. Dis. Publishing Co., 1913.

LARSON, JOHN A. Lying and Its Detection. Univ. of Chicago Press, 1932.

LASHLEY, K. S. Brain Mechanisms and Intelligence. Univ. of Chicago Press, 1929.

LEVY, DAVID M. and BECK, S. J. Am. Jour. of Orthopsychiatry, 4 (Jan.) 1934.

LEWIN, KURT. Dynamic Theory of Personality. McGraw Hill Book Co., Inc., New York and London. 1935.

LINDEMANN, E. Experimentalle Untersuchungen ueber das Entstehen und Vergehen von Gestalten. Psychologisch. Forschung. 2; 1922, 5.

MAYER-GROSS & STEIN. Pathologie der Wahrnehmung. Handbuch der Geisteskrankheiten, Erster Band, Vol. 1, Allgemeinen Teil I, p. 705.

Memoirs of the National Academy of Science, Vol. XV, p. 705.

NISSEN, H. W. A Field Study of the Chimpanzee. Comparative Psychological Monograph. VIII, 122 pp. 1931.

NISSEN, H. W., MACHOVER, S., and KINDER, E. A. A Study of Performance Tests Given to a Group of Native African Children. The British Jour. of Psychol. (General Section) XXV, Part 3, Jan. 1935.

ORTON, S. T. Word Blindness in School Children, Arch. of Neur. & Psych. 1925, 14, 581.

———— Reading, Writing and Speech Problems in Children. W. W. Norton Pub. Co. New York, 1936.

PINTNER, RUDOLF. The Feebleminded Child. In the Handbook of Child Psychology edited by Carl Murchison, Clark University, Worcester, Mass. 1933.

PÖTZL, O. Quoted by Schilder, P. Space, Time and Perception. Psyche. 14; 1934, 124.

———— Die Optisch-agnostischen Störungen. Wien, Deuticke. 1928. Aschaffenburg Handb. d. Psychiat. Spez. Teil, 3. Abt. 2, Halfte 2, Bd. 1.

POPPELREUTER, W. Zur Psychologie und Pathologie der Optischen Wahrnehmung. Ztschr. f. d. g. Neurol. & Psych. 83; 1923, 26.

POTTER, H. W. Schizophrenia in Children. Am. J. of Psych. 12 (May) 1933.

PRINZHORN, HANS. Bildnerei der Geisteskranken, Berlin. Julius Springer, 1922.

RIDDOCH, H. Dissociation in Visual Perception. Brain 40: 14, 1917.

RORSCHACH. Psychodiagnostik. Ernest Bircher, Berne, Switzerland, 1921.

ROSS, N. and SCHILDER, P. Tachistoscopic Experiments on the Perception of the Human Figure. Jour. of General Psychology. 10, 1934, 152.

RUSSELL, R. Cerebral Involvement in Head Injuries. Brain, 55; 549, 1932.

SANDER, F. Structure, Totality of Experience and Gestalt. In "Psychologies of 1930", ed. by C. Murchison, Worcester, Mass.

SCHEID, K. F. Die Psychologie des erworbenen Schwachsinns, Zentralbl. f. d. ges. Neurol. u. Psychiat. 67: 1, 1933.

SCHILDER, PAUL. Medizinische Psychologie für Aerzte und Psychologen. Berlin. Julius Springer. 1924.

———— Studien zur Psychologie und Symptomatologie der progressive Paralyse. Berlin, S. Karger, 1930.

———— Introduction to Psychoanalytical Psychiatry, Mono. No. 50. New York. Nerv. & Ment. Disease Pub. Co. 1928.

———— Experiments on Imagination, After Images and Hallucinations. Am. J. of Psych. 13; 1933, 597.

——— Psychic Disturbances after Head Traumas. Am. J. of Psych. 91; 155 (July) 1934.

——— Particular Types of Depressive Psychoses. Jour. of Nerv. & Ment. Dis. 80; pp. 501 and 658. 1934.

——— Space, Time and Perception, Psyche. 14; 1934, 124.

——— The Image and Appearance of the Human Body, Psyche Monographs No. 4. Kegan, Paul, Trench, Trubner & Co. Ltd. London. 1935.

SHINN, M. W. Notes on the Development of a Child. Univ. of California Studies, 1893–97, I. Pts. 1–4, p. 178.

SHERRINGTON, C. S. The Integrative Action of the Nervous System. Yale Univ. Press, New Haven, 1906.

STEIN, H. 37 Kongr. f. inn. Med. Wiesbaden, 1925.

STEIN, H. and VON WEIZSÄCKER, V. Ergebn. d. Physiol. 28, 657, 1928.

STENGEL. Deutsche Ztschr. f. Nervenh. 99, 33, 1927.

STORCH. Primitive Archaic Forms of Inner Experience and Thought in Schizophrenia. Nerve. & Ment. Dis. Mono. New York. 36.

STREET, R. A Gestalt Completion Test. Columbia Univ. Contribution to Education No. 481, 1931.

SULLY, J. Studies of Childhood, New York, Appleton, 1897. p. 527.

WERNICKE, C. The Complex of Symptoms of Aphasia, in Deutsche Klinik am Eingange des zwanzigsten Jahrhunderts in akademischen Vorlesungen, Berlin. Urban & Schwarzenberg, 1903.

WERTHEIMER, M. Studies in the Theory of Gestalt Psychology. Psychol. Forsch. 4; 1923, 300.

YERKES, R. M. The Mental Life of Monkeys and Apes. Behavior Monograph No. 3, New York, Harcourt, Brace & Co. 1916.

INDEX

Instructions

FOR THE USE OF

Visual Motor Gestalt Test

LAURETTA BENDER, M.A., M.D.

PSYCHIATRIC DIVISION, BELLEVUE HOSPITAL

NEW YORK

PUBLISHED BY

THE AMERICAN ORTHOPSYCHIATRIC ASSOCIATION, INC.

SINCE the publication in 1938 of Research Monograph No. 3 of the American Orthopsychiatric Association, *A Visual Motor Gestalt Test and Its Clinical Use,* there has been a demand for the test forms (Plate I) and instructions for their use.

The Test has been used as a maturational test in visual motor gestalt function in children (Plate II) (4), to explore retardation, regression, loss of function and organic brain defects in both adults and children (2, 3, 6, 7, 8), and to explore personality deviations, especially where there are regressive phenomena (5, 9). In the latter instance it fills the role of a non-social, neutral, apparently innocuous test in a battery of personality tests and has been found useful in the combat neuroses both diagnostically and in recording improvement. It has been used by clinical psychologists during World War II in army medical installations, such as in the neuropsychiatric services of general hospitals, convalescent units of station hospitals, mental hygiene units of replacement training centers.*

Reference should be made to the original monograph for the theoretical background, analysis of research and application of the test in the development of the gestalt function in the development of intelligence of children and in the diagnosis of the various clinical syndromes including mental deficiency, aphasias, the various organic brain disorders, the major psychoses, malingering and the psychoneuroses.

Gestalt function may be defined as that function of the integrated organism whereby it responds to a given constellation of stimuli as a whole, the response itself being a constellation or pattern or gestalt. Integration occurs by differentiation. The whole setting of the stimulus and the whole integrative state of the organism determines the pattern of response. Any pattern in any sensory field may be regarded as a potential stimulus. Any result-

---

* The Psychology and Social Work Section of the Mason General Hospital, of which Lt. Jules S. Holzberg is the chief, has been particularly active and given me considerable help in evaluating the test and formulating instructions.

3

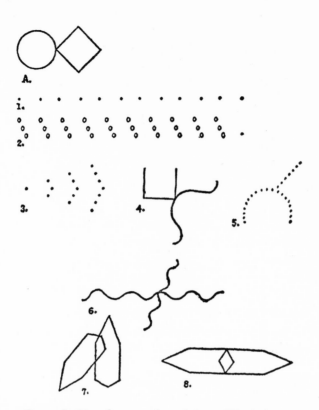

PLATE I. Test figures adapted from Wertheimer.

ing pattern is a sensory motor pattern. Every sensory pattern has its background and orientation in relation to spatial gestalt function. A series of sensory motor experiences involves temporal patterning. Any deviation in the total organism will be reflected in the final sensory motor pattern in response to the given stimulus pattern.

Nine of Wertheimer's (10) (see Plate I) original patterns used by him for research in visual gestalt psychology have been selected and are offered to the individual to be examined, for copying. Figure A which is readily experienced as a closed figure on a background is made up of contingent circle and diagonally placed square on a horizontal plane. This is used as an introductory figure. The figures 1 to 8 are then given in sequence. Sheets of

4

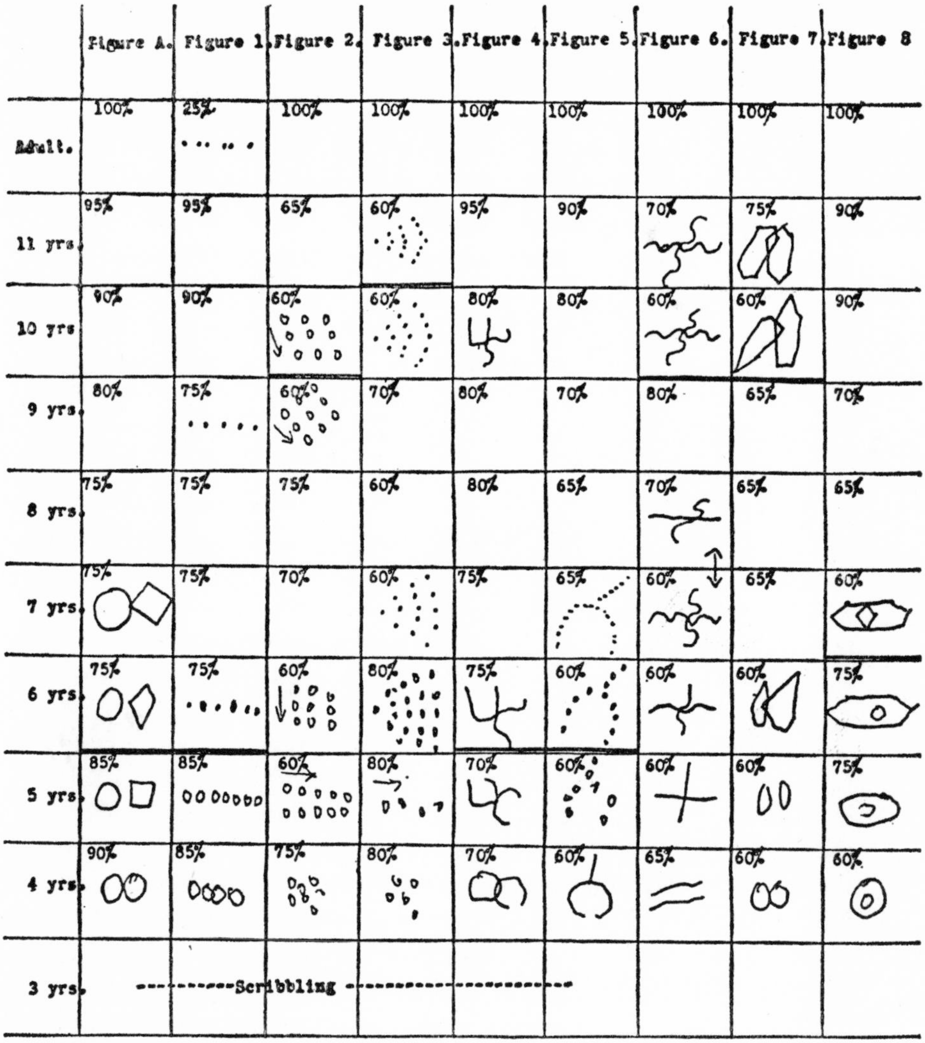

	Figure A	Figure 1	Figure 2	Figure 3	Figure 4	Figure 5	Figure 6	Figure 7	Figure 8
Adult.	100%	25%	100%	100%	100%	100%	100%	100%	100%
11 yrs.	95%	95%	65%	60%	95%	90%	70%	75%	90%
10 yrs	90%	90%	60%	60%	80%	80%	60%	60%	90%
9 yrs.	80%	75%	60%	70%	80%	70%	80%	65%	70%
8 yrs.	75%	75%	75%	60%	80%	65%	70%	65%	65%
7 yrs.	75%	75%	70%	60%	75%	65%	60%	65%	60%
6 yrs.	75%	75%	60%	80%	75%	60%	60%	60%	75%
5 yrs.	85%	85%	60%	80%	70%	60%	60%	60%	75%
4 yrs.	90%	85%	75%	80%	70%	60%	65%	60%	60%
3 yrs.	--------Scribbling -------------------------								

PLATE II. Summary of responses for each year of age in developing children. It may be used for evaluating maturational norms and levels of retardation and regression.

5

plain white unlined paper 8½″ by 11″ are used. One sheet is often enough but more may be necessary especially for individuals of the lower intellectual levels or those who are confused or disturbed. A pencil with an eraser should be used. There should be no mechanical aids such as a rule or coins, etc.

The cards may be presented one at a time laid on the table at the top of the sheet of paper correctly oriented and the individual to be tested should be told simply "Here are some figures (or designs) for you to copy; Just copy them the way you see them." It may be necessary to discourage the turning of the test card to some new position. If it is not easily discouraged, it should be permitted and noted. It is well to encourage the placing of the first figure near the upper left hand corner of the paper although if the suggestion is not readily accepted, it should not be insisted upon. The orientation of the figure on the background and in the series is also a part of the gestalt function. All other instructions should be non-committal. For example, if the question is asked if the dots should be counted, the answer should be, "It is not necessary but do as you like." Several attempts at any one figure may be permitted by leaving all trials on the record. Erasures to improve lines may be permitted but not encouraged.

There is no time limit on the test and the figures should not be removed until they are reproduced. Memory does not play a role in the test. Many individuals prefer to have all of the cards before them in a pile and look at them all and orient the whole test to the sheet of paper. This can be permitted but the test should start with figure A and run through series in order. Many succeed in orienting the whole test situation to its background on the sheet of paper without this initial exploration.

This is a clinical test and it should not be so rigidly formalized as to destroy its function which is to determine the individual's capacity to experience visual motor gestalten in a spatial and temporal relationship. Deviate behavior in the course of the test should be observed and noted. It never represents a test failure. Notes may be made on the test paper of anything unusual in the way the test is organized, in the manner and behavior of the individual being tested and his reaction to the test situation.

6

In a battery of tests, this test may often prove to be an effective introductory test as it is apparently innocuous and may make an anxious and uneasy individual feel more at ease in the test situation. It may be given at any other point in a battery and may also be a restful change between more verbal or emotionally weighted tests. If given when the individual is fatigued, this should be noted, as fatigue tends to exaggerate disturbances in the gestalt function, increasing perseverative tendencies or calling forth other energy saving processes or regressive tendencies. In my own clinical work with problem children, I usually use this gestalt test, the Goodenough drawing of a man, a few minutes of observation with some play material, observation of motor activity or play, a neurological examination and psychiatric interview. There is no regular order, however, each child requiring a different pattern for the total examination, depending on his clinical state at the time of the examination and many external circumstances.

Evaluation of the test does not depend upon the form of the reproduced figures alone but on their relationship to each other, to the spatial background, to the temporal patterning and the clinical setting. The original monograph should be referred to for the evaluation of the clinical use of this test.

BIBLIOGRAPHY

1. Bender, Lauretta. A Visual Motor Gestalt Test and Its Clinical Use. Research Monograph No. 3, American Orthopsychiatric Association, 1938.
2. Bender, Lauretta, Frank J. Curran, and Paul Schilder. *Organization of Memory Traces in the Korsakoff Syndrome.* Arch. Neurol. and Psychiat., 39: 1938, 452–487.
3. Curran, Frank J., and Paul Schilder. *Experiments in Repetition and Recall.* J. Genetic Psychol., 51: 1937, 163.
4. Fabian, A. A. *Vertical Rotation in Visual Motor Performance: Its relationship to Reading Reversals.* J. Educat. Psychol., March 1945, 129–154.
5. Hutt, Max L. *The Use of Projective Methods in Personality Measurement in Army Medical Installations.* J. Clinical Psychol., 1:1945, 134–140.
6. Schilder, Paul. *Mind: Perception and Thought in Their Constructive Aspects.* New York: Columbia University Press, 1942.
7. Schilder, Paul. *Notes on the Psychology of the Metrasol Treatment of Schizophrenia.* J. Nerv. and Ment. Disease., 89: 1939, 133.
8. Schilder, Paul. *Space, Time and Perception.* Psyche, 14: 1934, 124–139.
9. Spiegel, Herbert, Joel Shor, and Sidney Fishman. *An Hypnotic Ablation Technique for the Study of Personality Development.* Psychosomatic Medicine, 7:1945, 273–278.
10. Wertheimer, Max. *Studies in the Theory of Gestalt Psychology.* Psychol. Forsch., 4:1923, 300.